Patinas

FOR SILICON BRONZE

Patinas
FOR SILICON BRONZE

PATRICK V. KIPPER

Path Publications
Loveland, Colorado

Library of Congress Catalog Card Number 95-092327

ISBN 0-9647269-0-4

Second Edition
Second Printing 2003
Printed in Hong Kong by Regal Printing
http://www.regalprinting.com.hk

Patinas for Silicon Bronze is published by Path Publications in conjunction with Loveland Press.
Inquires should be directed to:
Loveland Press
P.O. Box 7001
Loveland, CO 80537 U.S.A.
1-(970)-593-9557
www.lovelandpress.com

Production Credits
Designed by LaVonne Kaseman
Illustrations by Christine Fries
Edited by Nancy Schmachtenberger & Mary Libbey
Cover Photograph by Joyce Jay
Photography of Patina Plates by Mel Schockner

Disclaimer: Every effort has been made to ensure that the information in this book, which is based on the Author's experience, is accurate. However, the Author and Publisher take no responsibility for any harm which may be caused by the use or misuse of any materials or processes mentioned herein, nor is any condition or warranty implied.

Dedicated
to
the memory of
Michael Radisich

Namastae

Acknowledgement

The author will always be truly grateful to Robert and Mary Zimmerman for their superb introduction to the art of bronze casting and artistic patination. Many thanks goes to Robert Zimmerman for sharing his superior knowledge of chemistry and metallurgical fundamentals used in patination, and to Mary Zimmerman for introducing the author to the artistic foundations associated with the coloring of bronze. The author feels honored to have been given the chance to learn from such individuals cognizant of their scientific and artistic skills.

The author would also like to thank all of the sculptors over the years for their confidence in his abilities as a patineur. A special thanks goes out to those artists that have given him the freedom to try new and different patina techniques. Without their trust and enthusiasm, his work would have been impossible.

A special thanks goes out to a dear friend, sculptor Glenna Goodacre for urging the author to explore new and different avenues of patination. Her artistic endeavors have become an inspiration to the author and his work.

The author is also grateful to sculptor Richard Greeves for sharing his enthusiastic approach to the art of patinas. His unique views and genuine sensitivity toward color has given the author a better understanding of bronze sculpture.

Sharing knowledge of bronze patination is often difficult to ascertain and therefore, the author would like to thank those master patineurs from Asia, Europe, and the Americas for their willingness to share and exchange secrets concerning chemical formulation in the coloring of bronze. This accumulated source of information is invaluable in developing a well rounded understanding and appreciation for the art of patination.

The author also wishes to acknowledge Bastiaan E. Cornelissen, P.E. from the Metallurgical and Materials Engineering Department of the Colorado School of Mines for his research into the history and fundamentals of silicon bronze. This knowledge helped to fill the gaps in understanding the various functions of silicon bronze.

A warm appreciation is extended to Nancy Schmachtenberger for her continuous support and patience during the writing of this book. Her persevering encouragement helped tremendously, and for that the author is truly grateful.

A special thanks goes out to Mr. Craig Nelsen and the people at Loveland Press, as well as the people at Regal Printing, for without their help and understanding, this book would still be only an idea. They were able to make it a reality.

Contents

Preface

"Patinas for Silicon Bronze" was written to give the sculptor working in bronze, a better understanding of the art of patination; to hopefully extend the palettes of fellow patineurs; to give guidelines to the novice art student who may be dabbling in bronze patination, and to introduce the public to the art of bronze coloration, which until recently, has been one of the most secretive of all art forms.

In most cultures around the world, the practice of enhancing metals by the utilization of color has been observed for centuries. Enriching the surface of certain metals such as copper and its various alloys, was to give a more desirable appeal to their surfaces. This tradition of coloration on bronzes (some of the more popular alloys of copper) was and still is one of the most exciting and diverse art forms which has the ability to bring attention to, or subdue its existence. This unique art form of bronze coloration is termed patination. Patinas are the end result of this coloring process and it is the person who is applying these patinas that carries the title of patineur.

Patinas for the surface of bronze sculpture are the most exciting of all forms of metal coloration, because not only do colors enhance a work of art, they have the ability to evolve emotion; hot reds for a passionate mood, cool blues to quiet the mind, rich greens to warm the heart, and a multitude of pattern and texture to excite the eye.

In many cases, the sculptor of fine art that is casting in bronze, will work closely with a patineur to help in the final execution toward a true work of art. Patinas have long been compared to the framing of a fine painting: It takes just the right one to enhance a particular piece. However, patinas have the capability to do much more than framing in that, on many pieces, the patina may become the central focus of attention.

Using various chemical potions in unique and traditional applications to produce coloration on bronze is indeed a fascinating art. It is hoped that the following information and color plates will give the reader a better understanding and appreciation for the art of patination, and hopefully give new and exciting avenues of coloration to the sculptor casting in silicon bronze. Also, may the following recipes help in the understanding of silicon bronze patination while enriching the palettes of fellow patineurs.

Ancient Chinese Ceremonial Wine Vessel
Contemporary Reproduction

PHOTOGRAPHER: MEL SCHOCKNER

CHAPTER ONE 1

Introduction

The art of patination may be thought of in terms of light, for light is color. On bronze sculpture, specific colors have the ability to enhance, enrich, or subdue its aesthetic beauty. Achieving a particular color for the makings of a true work of art is the art of patinas or patination, an almost unknown and, until recently, very secretive skill.

Historically, the art of patination has most commonly been defined as the coloration of metals and woods brought about by the oxidation of surfaces, caused by extended exposure to its immediate atmosphere. This definition is actually more of a description of one of two categories of patinas for bronze: natural and artificial.

Natural patinas are a result of timely residues discharged from chemical reactions to the bronze surface. Bronzes of antiquity discovered in cultural digs tend to have more of a blue coloration due to the high alkali levels tested in the surrounding soil as well as ammonia base compounds given off by the decomposition of organic materials. More of the true green to dark green and black patinas found on bronze from the Bronze Age have been found in digs of a more acidic or lower pH soil analysis. Along with other oxidizing minerals found in these surroundings, natural patinas then have quite a variety of color hue and value, not to mention texture. There is no way to achieve a true natural patina except with time itself. This is very important to a natural patina but very impossible for the sculptor, because it requires years to accomplish an end result.

Artificial patinas, on the other hand, have the advantage not only of creating similar results of a natural patina, they also have the ability to incorporate a wider range of color hue and depth not found in natural patinas, and this is accomplished almost immediately.

Customarily, there are three styles of artificial patinas: classical, traditional, and contemporary. These represent three different appearances that are categorized historically. The classical style is to represent natural patinas as closely as possible. By means of submerging the bronze into the elemental environments (attempting to assimilate the surroundings of buried artifacts), or by means of cold acidic washes, this style is not held to be a class of patinas reflecting properties of durability and longevity.

Traditional patinas are those that represent patina applications of the later renaissance on up to the late 19th and early 20th centuries. Many of these are achieved almost instantly, requiring heat as an aging and bonding process. They tend to reflect more subtle and subdued hues: dark browns, rich, transparent reds, dusty ocher finishes, and deep greens incorporating blacks. Many of these are applied in a layering fashion to resemble aged bronze. A traditional patina is a quiet, rich, and somewhat subdued patina, carrying with it signs of age, sometimes seen by intentional burnishing here and there to resemble repeated handling. These patinas, although simple in appearance, may be some of the more difficult to achieve. It takes a good eye and imagination to incorporate tasteful aging processes. However, they are the most respected and affluent styles of patinas for bronze sculpture.

On the other hand, contemporary patinas are those that represent a "stepping away" from tradition. This style of patinas is quite exciting, reflecting bright, iridescent, rich tones of transparency, or imitating a multitude of deep stone patterns found in marble and granite. This fashion of patination is probably the most unlimited of the three styles as a result of its endless color combinations, but also of its variety of medium reproduction, that is, marble, granite, concrete, wood, etc. Many applications of chemical compounds in this style are unorthodox to the traditional school of thought. Where the brush is the prime applicator of compounds in the traditional style, the contemporary style makes use of such things as squirt bottles, spatter guns, etc. The only downside of this style is that many contemporary patinas are difficult and, in some cases, impossible to reproduce. Therefore, when going into this field of patinas, it is necessary to accept this fact and enjoy the exciting results.

Recipes listed in this book are more of a concentration of traditional and contemporary patina styles. They are by far the most popular world wide and, as a result of their application by use of heat, they are also the most durable. They have all been used time and time again with little discrepancy, although please keep in mind that there are variances to each patina. There are factors that are so numerous in the patina process as to give a sense of individualism to each piece. This individualism may only be seen by the patineur as a result of his or her intimate relationship with the patinaed surface. Nevertheless, it is one of the most exciting aspects about these patina styles; that is, as a sculptor you have the ability to visualize your piece in different values of the same patina. It's exciting to the patineur as well, for he or she is fortunate to see how many different variations he or she has on a theme or chemical combination.

The main factor in the excitement of achieving these patinas is by the use of heat. Normally, traditional and contemporary patinas are developed by two types of chemical application: hot and cold. Cold applications are those whereby the surface of the metal is at room temperature as well as the chemical compounds used to achieve true coloration. Some colors are immediate, while others may take days or even months to achieve. Besides this drawback, cold patinas tend to be much more fragile—merely sitting on the surface of the bronze. By touching the bronze surface, the patina may be disturbed and ruin an otherwise beautiful job. On the other hand, hot patina processes are those where the surface of the bronze is hot in order to apply chemical compounds for inducing coloration. Not only is the coloration more immediate, but it is much more durable. However, both of these processes need to be sealed from the environment, or they may tend to go natural.

The two most important tools in the art of patination are understanding and patience. The ability to understand what the chemical compounds available to you can accomplish, while understanding what the sculptor is requesting, is of great importance. Patience is the other, and probably the most important, tool one can have in the art of patinas. Some things turn out and some don't, even when you understand every step of a particular patina process that you have done fifty times. Relax and enjoy this field of alchemy we fondly call the art of patination. It can be a most exciting art field of discovery and reward.

CHAPTER TWO

Bronze—A History

The history of man's civilization has been measured by his ability to manufacture as well as use materials found in his surroundings. The use of stone was the first and most obvious material man had in his possession. Tools as well as weapons have been found in numerous locations around the world, attesting to this. Following the Stone Age, there's a small and sometimes overlooked age of prehistoric man called the Copper Age. This segment in man's history is sometimes left out or included in the following age—the Bronze Age. The Copper Age is a small, but important time in the evolution of man striving toward the Bronze Age. Many theories arise as to the importance of the Copper Age, but we can see that it was most important to the development of the Egyptian culture as well as areas of Cypress and Mesopotamia. In Egypt, the Copper Age was signified by the building of the great pyramids. In time, as the supply of copper diminished and the demand increased, it became a product of the trade throughout the prehistoric era. One theory is that in Mesopotamia, the people were using tin as an alternative metal. By trading with other cultures, the creation and use of bronze came about.

Bronze soon became the metal of choice, seeing that it was a much stronger alloy, perfect for weapons as well as much stronger for tools, cooking utensils, etc. The edges of copper swords were no match against the stronger edges of their bronze counterparts, and the bronze ax outlasted one made from copper. The regarded date for the beginnings of this metal evolution was around 2200 B.C.E. in the Mesopotamian area.

This theory of metallurgy and time in history was long accepted as the norm until in 1966 when an American sociologist came across rims of burial jars along a path in northeast Thailand.

"He alerted the Thai Fine Arts Department, which formed a team to dig at the site. While excavating the burial pots, numerous bronze objects were also found. The clay pots were found to date from perhaps 3000 B.C.E. What is suggested was that the bronze artifacts buried with them would have to be of nearly equal antiquity. If it were true, it meant that Thailand, not the Middle East, had opened the Bronze Age—700 years before Mesopotamia."[1]

Whichever theory we wish to follow is of little concern to the actual history of patination. However, as of the late 20th century, the popular theory is that the Bronze Age started around 3000 B.C.E., and though bronze later declined as a choice of weaponry metal due to the onset of the Iron Age, which started around 1000 B.C.E., it was to remain the most popular in the casting and hammering of artwork as well as cooking utensils.

Other cultures that flourished during the Bronze Age were China, India, and Greece. They all produced fine examples of weapons and tools cast in bronze as well as a treasure chest of sculpture and other decorative arts. In China, for example, ritual vessels were being cast. In Greece, fine sculpture representing the Greek Pantheon, as well as everyday whimsical objects, were in use, and in Mesopotamia, we have found some of the most beautifully cast and hammered bronze weaponry ever produced.

CHAPTER THREE 3

History of Patinas

It is from this Bronze Age artwork of antiquity that we find the foundations of patination. In China there have been mirrors exhumed from tombs that indicate chemical compounds were deliberately placed on the surface of the cast bronze. It is unknown if this was done to indicate social rank or merely to enhance the beauty of the object itself. Nevertheless, it is proof that intentional coloration of bronze goes back almost as far as casting itself. Other cultures have found indications of artificial patination or coloration on bronze as well. India and Greece have both discovered traces of foreign pigments that indicate the bronze sculptures may have been painted with egg, water, and pigment mixtures. Whether this was done for aesthetic or religious purposes is unknown.

Many weapons of the bronze era also show signs of a deliberate firing or of the building up of "heat scale" layers on the surface. Whether this was for retardation of the natural patina process or for something of a more spiritual nature is a mystery. Natural patinas on these bronze weapons are much thinner, and the colors tend to be more subdued, as opposed to those bronze art objects that would have been used for more aesthetic purposes.

As many of these prehistoric bronzes were being unearthed, the natural patinas that had developed on the surfaces came to be admired by the late Greek and Roman Empires. Attempts were made at this early time in our history to recreate the beautiful coloration of those prehistoric bronzes. There were many other mixtures (such as salt and vinegar or ammonia) used in "burial patinas" to achieve similar results. Along with these common recipes were many others that had been developed. During the decline of the Roman Empire and upon entering the Dark Ages of the western world, many of these recipes were lost. These are some of the first attempts of artificial patinas found in the western world. It isn't until the emergence of the alchemist in the middle of the Dark Ages that we find a new spark of interest in the coloration of metal. This interest was based more on the search to change menial metals into gold (or at least resembling the surface coloration) than it was for its mere historical and aesthetic reproductivity.

Later in the Dark Ages and into the beginnings of the European Renaissance, the true blossoming of bronze patination came to be, especially as an art form. Not only were patineurs reproducing the effects of natural patinas, but they were also creating new and more lasting looks by introducing new innovations such as wax and oil sealers, used to prolong the effects of patination on the surfaces of bronze sculpture. As the Renaissance in Europe continued to develop, so did the alchemy of bronze patinas.

As gold leafing or "gilding" became more popular during the later Renaissance and Baroque eras, the art of patination declined and did not rejuvenate until the early 19th century. All of this time, as alchemy was becoming more of a science, the art of bronze patination was still being kept more of an alchemy. This tradition still carries on somewhat even today.

Continuing on through the 19th and into the 20th centuries, countries such as France and Italy excelled in expanding the patina palette. During the 19th century the French were introducing deep, rich, translucent colors. A wide range of coloration was also being achieved by the use of pigmented varnishes which, in many cases, were to resemble transparent patinas that were achieved chemically. The Italians were creating beautiful marbling concepts as well as layering patinas for rich and interesting depth.

Entering the 20th century, as the science of chemistry grew, so did the palette of the patineur. Consequently, today the art of patination in the western world is experiencing an evolution in expanding the palette of not only hue and value, but also depth and even texture. This not only gives the sculptor more choices of finish, it also allows the artist to express his or her work as never before in history.

A SHORT ASIAN HISTORY

As mentioned in the chapter on the history of bronze, some of the first recorded attempts at artificial coloration of bronze were found in tombs discovered in China. Backs of a few mirrors had traces of pigmentation that would not have been produced by the atmosphere of an enclosed tomb, unlike those ritual vessels discovered in the same tombs that have beautiful encrusted natural patinas. This discovery has produced theories as to the possibility that China may have been one of the first cultures to introduce the art of artificial patination.

In the beginnings, cultures such as China and India did not attempt to artificially patina their bronze surfaces. There are exceptions to this, however, in India, where pigmented mixtures were (and still are) poured over bronze castings of deities for religious purposes. Most bronze castings were left in their raw states, allowing their surfaces to age naturally from their exposure to hand oils. From the beginnings of the Christian era to the early 12th century, there is little evidence of artificial patination. "The custom of artificially patinating bronzes in imitation of the finish of the buried artifacts that did survive from the Shang and Chou periods probably first occurred at this time in the 12th century Chin period, as part of the attempt to recreate the lost heritage of these earlier periods."[2] As time went on, this art became more and more refined, not only expanding on new coloration of metal, but also developing new finishes for metal.

India, too, was experiencing new avenues of coloration, though most were kept somewhat subdued, except for the religious applications of certain bright colors painted on the surface of bronze deities. Oils were also used in religious practices, which in turn helped to darken and somewhat seal the surfaces. As these bronzes aged, they took on darker hues of browns and blacks.

Japan, although a late comer to the Bronze Age developed many new and innovating processes of coloration. They introduced coloration based on new metals being introduced into the casting of bronze, such as silver, gold, arsenic, and antimony. As a result of these new metal alloys, certain recipes were developed incorporating acidic juices from certain plants. Layering of metals was also important to the history of patination in Japan as they would layer metals one on top of the other and then, using certain acid washes, would bring out color on under layers of metal, leaving upper layers untouched, producing new concepts of depth.

It wasn't until later in the 19th and early 20th centuries that a new revolution in the coloration of bronze occurred due to a new-found interest in the arts and antiquities of Asia by the western world. Many new as well as old recipes were then used in the creation of "new antiques." As a result, many patineurs of Asia have become the masters in the world of classical and traditional patinas. They have created such techniques for aging bronzes that even masters in the field of Asian antiquities have been fooled. As a result, many museums around the world have innocently acquired fake antique bronzes due the expert artistry of the Asian patineur.

The Patineur

The term "patineur" comes from the French and means one that is an artist of patination. The art of patination has carried with it many traditions. In most areas of the world, historically, there was the master patineur and the apprentice. A student patineur never accepted the title of "master patineur" until he had acquired at least seven years of apprenticeship in this three-dimensional art. This tradition still exists today. Patina recipes were and still are without a doubt, well protected secrets of the master patineur. It was tradition for the master to pass this knowledge on to his son; for many families this was their livelihood and had been for generations. If there was no son, it was passed on to this senior apprentice. Although this practice has been dying out in the west, it is still found in many parts of Asia today.

Traditionally, it is taboo to ask a master patineur or apprentice for his or her secret recipes. It has always been left up to the patineur to divulge this information if he or she chooses. Remember, for centuries, foundries and individual patineurs have used certain patinas as a trademark of their work. This is innocently overlooked by many westerners as a result of their lack of knowledge of this tradition. There are times, however when individuals are merely admiring a patina, and this then is usually taken as a compliment.

There is another new tradition to the art of patination which has evolved due to the production of the personal camera, and that is taking pictures of a patineur and patina while it is in process. Once again, it is a way of disclosing many patina secrets that would otherwise be secretive. Also, on a more technical note, patineurs use many chemical compounds that are considered "light sensitive," and flashes from cameras can destroy these processes. Therefore, patineurs will usually stop their applications until the camera is tucked away. Always ask not only to watch but ask also if photos are allowed before pulling out a camera. More secrets have been lost and patinas destroyed due to the presence of a camera.

The most traditional role of the patineur probably is one of understanding. Not only must he or she be sensitive to the ideas of the sculptor, he or she must also be sensitive to the art of bronze sculpture itself. The patineur is probably one of the most important people in the career of the sculptor in bronze. As a result of this close working relationship between sculptor and patineur, the field of patinas has become a very personal one. To decipher color choices in another's mind may take years of experience. For many sculptors, their concentration is not in color but rather in the design, form, balance, and movement of a piece. It is up to the patineur to help decipher whether the sculptor wishes to accentuate or subdue any of these aspects of the bronze. The role of the patineur, therefore, is not only to help the sculptor in choosing color schemes, but also to help in the creation of a work of art.

CHAPTER FIVE

Bronze Alloys

Copper is the main element used in the manufacturing of all bronze and brass alloys. These non-ferrous groups have been developed over the centuries in response to cultural needs, where such requirements as strength, formability, and resistance to corrosion are necessary. Copper itself is somewhat resistant to corrosion; that is why it is formed and used in transferring chemical compounds such as water. Copper, as a pure element, is somewhat soft and pliable, which makes its strength factor somewhat low. By mixing other elements such as tin, zinc, lead, aluminum, nickel, silver, and, more recently, silicon to copper, the "tensile" strength is increased.

As mentioned in the chapter on "The History of Bronze," tin was the first element used in the creation of bronze. Its hardness and ability to hold an edge made it superior over pure copper for such things as weaponry, cooking utensils, and storage vessels for water and wine. As a result of its high tensile strength, this copper-tin alloy became a favorite choice for metals involved in man's architecture as well.

Consequently, as newer requests for bronze grew, and in some cases, tin supplies dwindled, different copper alloys were developed. On the artistic side, newer alloys were produced using such elements as zinc, lead, arsenic, silver, and even gold. These various combinations were a result of a search for different colors and richness not found in the traditional copper-tin alloys. On the commercial front, these newer bronzes gave even more of a variety of tensile strength and corrosion resistance needed in their newer and ever expanding functions. As a result, as history changed, so did the development of bronze metallurgy.

Today, a wide range of bronze alloys have been developed for use according to their needs and desires. Just as artistic requirements have changed from culture to culture, so have the bronze alloys. This is most prominent in the casting process of these alloys in which sculptural forms are desired. Historically, these desires were based on metal coloration; that is, copper-tin gave a dull pinkish color, copper-tin-zinc gave more of a yellow cast, and lead was added to give a softer rose coloration to copper-tin-zinc. Arsenic and silver were used for lavenders, grays, and blues.

In many cases, these various colors would not be seen until the cast bronze surface was burnished and/or polished. As copper tends to oxidize or tarnish quite easily, so do many of its alloys. When these bronze alloys were brought to a polish, the oxidizing process became more evident, bringing about natural changes in the color of the metal. Many chemical treatments were used to inhibit this reaction. In some cases this process of oxide retardation worked, but, in many cases, it increased the process, causing more and different coloration effects. Various artificial patinas were established to either hold or enhance the metal coloration or to change it completely. Many bronze alloys change color at a different rate, which gave the artist more choices of coloration. Some of these newer alloys were better for casting purposes while others were more appropriate for fabrication.

Casting quality of bronze alloys became the primary goal of most sculptors and architects. Some alloys cast better than others. By experimentation, most cultures found what alloy mixtures worked best for them. Mineral availability also was of great importance in the production of various bronze alloys from culture to culture.

The following alloys listed are a direct result of the search and discovery of castable bronze alloys which are still used today. The following alloys are categorized in a number sequence with copper being represented by the first number, followed by various other minerals which compose these particular alloys.

TRADITIONAL BRONZE 90-10

Traditionally, bronze was composed of 90% copper and 10% tin. This alloy ratio varied considerably from time to time and culture to culture, depending on style, casting requirements, and availability of these minerals. This metal combination is the foundation from which all other bronze alloys were developed.

Tin is what separates bronze from the "brass" family. Where bronze is composed of copper and tin, brass is a mixture of copper and zinc. This combination not only makes brass more brittle than that of bronze, it also is what gives brass its yellowish, amber color.

Traditional bronze has been used since its inception in the casting of sculpture in cultures from Egypt to China. This alloy in great variances is still used primarily in Asian cultures such as Thailand and Indonesia, where the element of tin is still quite available. It accepts artificial patinas well and changes little with time. This alloy was (and still is) cast quite thin, which produces a casting that is light weight and therefore, easy to manipulate from place to place. However, the final casting may be of inferior quality to those cast from more recent alloys.

RED BRASS 85-5-5-5

European bronze or red brass is a metal combination of 85% copper, 5% tin, 5% zinc, and 5% lead. This alloy has been used in the production of cast bronze sculpture for centuries throughout Europe. Coloration of this bare bronze when burnished or buffed gives a rose or pinkish hue to the surface. Because of this alloy mixture, artificial patinas were (and still are) applied with great ease, with the finished coloration changing little with time.

As a result of the increasing cost of tin over the years and the toxicity associated with lead, this alloy is being slowly replaced by other alloys that are not only cheaper, but less hazardous as well. Other modern problems associated with red brass: the casting quality may not be as good as newer alloys, and welded areas, when assembly is required, tend to hold different color than that of the surrounding cast bronze. This, in many cases, affects the final choice of patina coloration. Opaque patinas with solid base coats are usually a good choice when attempting to hide this welding problem.

ASIAN BRONZE 90-5-5

This bronze alloy ranges considerably from culture to culture as a result of its mineral availability and color desired. Roughly, Asian bronze is composed of 90% copper, 5% tin, and 5% zinc. Some cultures such as India developed and used bronzes that were more of a brass, consisting of as much as 40% zinc. This made for a yellow casting, resembling that of yellow gold. India and Nepal still use these alloys with great success. The casting quality is not as good as many of the other alloys mentioned, however, tending to produce larger areas of shrink and porosity. Artificial patinas work quite well on this alloy, but with quite different results as compared with those used on European bronze.

SILICON BRONZE

The field of silicon bronze alloys is quite large due to its wide range of diversity. Its development is a result of greater demands for higher tensile strength, forgability and formability, where casting quality is of prime importance. "Developed in the 1920's as a spark-resistant alloy for explosives manufacturing equipment, it became widely accepted, especially in the USA, for chemical plants. Subsequently, overtaken in this area by aluminum bronzes and stainless steels, it is now best known as an alloy used for sculpture and marine fittings."[3]

"Within the past several years there has been a commercial division of the silicon bronzes into two general types which are known as grades A and B."[4] Silicon bronzes rated in Grade "A" have a higher ratio of silicon as opposed to bronzes falling under the "B" rating, which tend to have lower silicon levels and higher copper levels.

In the manufacturing of bronze sculpture, high silicon rated bronze, or silicon "A," has become the alloy of choice. Everdur is the name given to this group of bronze alloys used in this particular industry. The everdur alloy that is most commonly used in the Americas is 95-4-1. This ratio consists of 95% copper, 4% silicon, and 1% manganese, with traces of other elements such as iron. "Its combination of corrosion resistance, strength, resilience, formability, and weldability make it one of the most widely used of the copper metals."[5] Almost perfect castings may be achieved using this metal, making it the metal of choice for the western world sculptor. Many art foundries in Europe and many parts of Asia are now pouring this alloy with exceptional results.

Silicon bronze is usually more difficult to patina than other alloys mentioned, because of the high copper content that is resistant to corrosion and of the silicon used, which is a color retardent. Common reagent metal salts may react slower and with quite different results on silicon bronze. Patinas may tend to change or disappear completely from the bronze surface due to this alloy makeup. Unlike tin and lead, which will oxidize and transfer color easily, silicon will inhibit such reactions. Remember, one of the primary functions of silicon bronze is to resist corrosion better than other bronze alloys. This is only one of the many reasons why patina recipes formulated for other bronze alloys will not function as well on silicon bronze, especially over time. Certain chemical compounds can be very unstable on everdur bronze. Because of its high copper content, silicon bronze may cause cupric nitrate salts to change from a beautiful blue-green to a reddish-rust color. This change is usually caused by a reduction of the copper salts into "dicuprous oxides." Although this chemical compound is one of the basic metallic salts used in the art of patination, different procedures are recommended for its application on silicon bronze.

The makeup of this alloy is also why the patinas on its surface should be well sealed from the environment, as these patinas will tend to change, usually to a darker hue. In many cases the traditional wax treatment alone will not suffice. Lacquers and varnishes are recommended for sealing the surface of everdur as they will protect the patinas much longer and with greater resiliency than waxes. A drawback to lacquers and varnishes is that they tend to leave a shiny or glossy finish to the bronze surface, and, therefore, waxes are usually applied over these finishes in order to tone down the shine and make for a more traditional look. The alteration of chemical compound applications and sealers for silicon bronze will be discussed later in much more detail.

Since everdur is the primary bronze alloy of choice for casting quality and weldability, the problems associated with coloring this alloy has been secondary. With increasing demands for a wider variety of color and depth in bronze patinas, it has been up to the patineur to develop new procedures for a more traditional look (as well as creating new, long-lasting concepts for more contemporary appearances) on this new alloy to the world of bronze which we call everdur.

CHAPTER SIX

Metal Surface Preparation

Preparing the surface of cast metal is of prime importance to the application and final result of a patina. This preparation is twofold; not only does it have the ability of reflecting light for a glossy finish, which brings out depth in transparent contemporary patinas or dulling finishes for more traditional effects, it also cleans the surface, which enables the copper within the bronze to accept the reactions of chemical compounds from the patina process. There are many ways in which to go about this preparation. They are all based on first, the casting itself, and second, the sculpted surface—that is, smooth or moderate to heavily modeled.

This chapter begins with a bronze that is freshly cast, blasted to remove the investment material, and welded (if assembly is required) with the welds "chased" in order to make these areas of the casting resemble no weld at all. The bronze casting itself may or may not require much in the way of finishing depending on the casting as well as the patina chosen.

The casting will always have some defects, whether they are in the form of porosity (many small pin holes in a cluster, also called spongy metal as it may resemble the surface of a sponge), or cracks, caused in many cases by unknown sources. "Although the careful use of appropriate casting methods will help to minimize the occurrence of holes caused by trapped gas, and clean working methods will reduce the likelihood of particles of foreign matter being trapped in the melt, it is virtually impossible to produce castings that are entirely free of these casting defects."[6] These imperfections may or may not be seen while in the chasing process; however, they have the ability to come to the foreground during the application of the patina, destroying or at the least, altering the finished product. Some of the techniques listed for finishing the surface of the bronze will either hide or accentuate casting imperfections. Therefore, care should be taken when deciding what finish will work best not only to hide these imperfections, but also to enhance the patina which will be chosen for a particular piece.

There are basically three finishes to choose from when finishing the surface of the bronze for patination: blasting, sanding, or polishing. These finishes are used in most art foundries world wide. The finishes listed are a direct result of light reflection or refraction. Some will tend to lighten a bronze while others will tend to darken and even hide detail.

BLASTING

Historically, probably the newest form of finish and cleaning on the surface of bronze is by means of blasting. This process is accomplished by bombarding the bronze surface with various grits (grain size) of sand propelled by compressed air. This process is usually accomplished within a metal cabinet with some sort of attached dust collection implemented. However, there are times when the size of the bronze prohibits this and then outdoor blasting may be required. Blasting with sand has become most common in the finishing and cleansing of bronze sculpture as seen in most American art foundries and independent metal finishing establishments. It cleans the surface faster than most other processes, and it also has the advantage of "toothing" or roughening the surface in order to allow chemical compounds sufficient time to react. It also leaves a nice matte finish on which to apply patinas.

Deciding which grit size to use on a certain project is of great importance. Sand is measured by the size of the individual grains of sand; that is, 80 grit is considered to be very large, while 180 grit is very small or fine. Using 80 grit sand will tend to roughen the surface of the bronze. It may even change or wipe out fine detailed texture. It can also disclose areas of porosity and other casting defects that may not have been seen before this treatment. Blasting with 80 grit does have an advantage, however, of hiding or blending welded and chased areas of the surface. As a blasting medium, 80 to 100 grit is also most cost effective on large castings. These large sand grits are never recommended if polishing is required as the end result because it will leave a grit or toothing on the surface of the bronze that is too deep to buff out. Dark, transparent patinas will usually be the result of this treatment as well as a flat, non-glossy finish.

Smaller grits of sand which are used in the blasting process tend to leave a finer, softer look and feel to the surface, disturbing it as little as possible. A 180 grit is highly recommended for cleaning the surface for this reason. Also, 180 grit is also the medium used in cleaning many of the following recipes. As a result of modern technology, the metal finisher (chaser) and patineur have a variety of sand grits of different mediums to choose from. An 80 grit is most commonly sold to the art foundry business in the form of "silica" sand (silicon dioxide—SiO_2). It may be purchased in somewhat finer grits or grains as well, such as 100 to 120 grits. Care should be observed when blasting with these mediums as with all blasting mediums, because exposing these silicon dioxide airborne particles to the tissues of the lungs can result in silicosus, a chronic disease which may result in contributing to early and untimely death.

Finer blasting grits may be purchased in the form of aluminum oxide (Al_2O_3), also known as alumina. This medium is most superior to silica sand in the cleaning and preparation of the bronze surface, especially when using 150 to 180 grit sizes. Its toothing reaction is much smaller and does not penetrate the surface as deeply as silicon sand. Being almost as hard as diamond itself, aluminum oxide will not break down or "powder" as readily as silica sand. This advantage, as well as the benefit of its minimal disturbance of the bronze surface itself, has made it a favorite choice for art foundries and patineurs. The downside to aluminum oxide is that it is costly, as blasting mediums go, and tend not to be very cost effective for large projects.

There are other mediums as well that are used in the cleaning and preparation of the bronze surface. Glass beading is quite a popular choice as it is cost effective and can give more of a sheen to the surface finishing process. The result of blasting with glass beads tends to give a "rounder" toothing (more of a microscopic concave indentation), which reflects or bounces light back as compared with other sands, which tend to give more of a sharp, somewhat angular pattern not seen by the naked eye but resulting in a matte finish, engulfing light. The disadvantage of using glass beads is that they tend to break down or "powder" rather quickly and so must be replaced often.

Other blasting mediums available on the open market for finishing and cleaning bronze are walnut shells, new synthetic sand compounds and even water. Water blasting is just now becoming available to the field of art bronze manufacturing. In the art of patination, blasting with water can be a disadvantage in that unwanted chemical compounds in the water may be deposited on the surface which may inhibit a clean reaction from the patina chemicals. A great advantage to this new system, however, is that it is environmentally safe since dust or airborne particles are eliminated. As water is used more and more in the field of art bronze, it will most certainly be refined to become a beneficial source of cleaning and preparing the surface for patination. This process has been witnessed by the author many times, but has never been used personally.

All of the media used in blasting should be used with as little compressed air pressure as possible: 60 to 70 PSI (pounds per square inch) are the highest ratings recommended for blasting most bronze surfaces. More than 70 PSI will tend to drive the particles of sand deeper into the surface, causing unwanted and unnecessary roughness to the finish. Not only does this higher pressure have the ability to embed particles of sand into the bronze, it also has the tendency to disclose casting defects. Therefore, always blast the surface of bronze with PSI ratings of not more than 70 PSI.

PICKLING OR ACID BATH TREATMENTS

Pickling or acid bath treatments are other ways of toothing the bronze surface by means of etching while at the same time cleaning the surface. This process is usually achieved by submerging the bronze in an acid bath, or is applied to the surface with natural, fibered rags. With today's technologies for metal surface cleaning and finishing, there is really no need for the use of acid baths. This surface treatment is more suitable in the manufacturing of jewelry, where the bath is kept considerably smaller. The extreme physical dangers and environmental concerns involved with acid baths on bronze sculpture of a size over two inches make it obsolete. Another reason why this cleansing treatment is not recommended for bronze castings is that residues from the bath may become trapped in small inclusions and other casting defects not seen by the naked eye. Even with thorough rinsing and acid neutralizing, these residues from the acid bath could leech back out later in a spotting pattern and not only disturb the finished patina, but bring attention to the quality of the casting itself.

Take extreme care when working with acid baths. These strong corrosive acids are harmful to all parts of the body, so protection must be observed. Required equipment that must be worn while dealing with acids are: acid gas/organic vapor rated respirator, eye goggles, a clean face shield, rubber gloves, and an apron. Wear long pants and long shirt sleeves as well as shoes for protection.

Good ventilation is required when mixing an acid bath solution for cleaning bronze. The MIXING and APPLICATION of pickling solutions must be done OUTDOORS or under ACID HOODS, and, if possible, at temperatures above 60 degrees.

Before dealing with acids, carefully read all Material Safety Data Sheets which accompany your acid purchase. The safety and handling of acids are the responsibility of the user.

Pickling solutions, as well as all chemicals used in the art of patination, should be kept safely out of reach of children and pets. Severe harm resulting in death could result in the mishandling of acid baths. A standard acid bath for bronze surface cleaning consists of the following:

	1 part	70% nitric acid to
	10 parts	distilled water
or	1 part	sulfuric acid to
	10 parts	distilled water

ALWAYS ADD ACID SLOWLY TO WATER, NEVER WATER TO ACID!!!

Place pieces to be cleaned in acid bath and etch for around three minutes. Allow more time if pieces are extra dirty. Then remove pieces from solution and rinse them thoroughly with water. A rinse by submerging or soaking the bronze is highly recommended as this will help draw the trapped acids to the surface, where they may be neutralized. Bronzes should be placed in many fresh water bathes in order to achieve a clean, neutral effect. If there are many stains left on the metal that did not come off using the solutions given above, a stronger acid bath may be required. Be careful when strengthening these solutions, as damage to the surface may result.

Disposing of acid baths can also be a nuisance. Always check with and follow your state and local regulations dealing with the disposal of these baths.

SANDING

Sanding has great advantages to the finishing of bronze prior to patination. This process not only cleans the surface, but also gives a choice of satin or high gloss, reflective qualities. The method of sanding is probably one of the oldest forms of metal finishing. All cultures involved in the Bronze Age used various grits of sand at one time or another in the finishing of bronze. Sanding was, and still is, the necessary foundation of rich, deeply transparent patinas.

Sanding the bronze surface is approached basically in two ways: mechanically and manually. Thanks in part to innovations from the auto body industry, mechanical sanding is by far the easiest and quickest way to a finished product. Either pneumatic driven or electric sanders work well. Pneumatic sanders are preferred in art foundries because of the variance of RPM control, as well as numerous other factors. Electrical sanders work just as well for preparing the bronze for patina; however, they are preferred on large broad areas as they tend to "facet" smaller bronzes.

There are many sanding products available to the artist, ranging in grit size and wheel or disc diameter. When sanding the bronze surface, it is customary to start with a courser grit and progress to finer ones for smoother surfaces. It is usually unnecessary to start with any grit coarser than 180 for final sanding. Coarser grits may tend to disturb or even destroy the cast and chased surface. Experienced metal chasers will know what grits to use on individual surfaces. When in doubt, always check with an experienced metal chaser, as he or she will know the final outcome.

When purchasing these sanding products, one has the choice of either cone or disc designs. Disc sanders tend to cover more surface at a faster rate, but are unable to get into small, tight areas. This is where sanding cones are advantageous. As a result of their shape, they can reach into small, tight areas of the sculpted surface, making for a more universally smooth finish.

Various grits of sandpaper or emery cloth, sold in the forms of cones or discs, are measured the same way as when purchasing blasting sand. These are the same grit sizes used in blasting, but they have been adhered onto the surface of paper or cloth usually by means of industrial glues. They work well in the sanding of the bronze surface, but under high RPMs they tend to break down or rip quickly. Lower RPMs will, in most cases, extend the life of the disc or cone.

There are many synthetic products on the market today that also work well in the finishing of metal. Companies such as 3M™ make a wide variety of abrasive products, such as ROLOC™ sanding discs and Scotch-Brite™ handpads, where the sands, both natural and synthetic, are embedded in a mesh pad backing. These pads work well for finishing bronze. Their flexibility gives them an advantage over paper discs when finishing three-dimensional surfaces. The 3M Very Fine Blue ROLOC™ 2" and 3" discs were used for finishing many of the Patina Plates.

If paper is preferred, whether in cone or disc shape, a 320 grit is recommended for the last step in mechanical sanding. A 220 grit is also acceptable as a final sanding prior to the application of the many patinas listed.

Always move as quickly as possible when mechanically sanding a bronze surface. Bronze is a relatively soft metal and if one's actions are slow or sluggish, faceting may be produced. Always move in a sweeping motion wherever possible. It is best to crisscross the sanding pattern in order to break any sanding lines that may occur. Then sand in a circular motion until the desired finish is achieved.

There are also many buffing compounds that are available to the artist which make an excellent sanding medium. Be positive that the compounds being used are greaseless. There are many water-based buffing compounds available. They are applied in conjunction with buffing pads or wheels. These wheels are usually made of many layers of cloth sewn or glued together. This makes for a softer applicator of the buffing compounds to the metal surface.

Buffing compounds or "rouges" are composed of various sand grits, either natural or synthetic, suspended in a thick paste. Everything from a rough satin finish (180 grit) to a smoother gloss (320 grit) to even a mirrored polish can be achieved by means of these buffing compounds. In preparing the surface for the application of patinas, a 320 grit is the finest grit recommended. A 180 to 220 grit is sufficient for the following patinas listed. Finishes where a mirrored polish is achieved are not used in the patina process as there is no toothing left on the bronze surface and, therefore, patinas will tend to flake off either during or after the patination process.

One main drawback in the use of buffing compounds on the surface of bronze in the preparation of patination is that these rouges tend to leave residues that may become embedded in the textured surfaces, only to reappear later (either during or after the patina process) as discoloration in the finished product. These residues can sometimes be cleaned out of textured areas of the bronze sculpture by using organic solvents. Please read the section on organic solvents before attempting this process.

Hand sanding or manual sanding is by far the oldest form of smoothing any surface. It requires much more time and energy than mechanical sanding. The traditional way of hand sanding the surface of the bronze is quite simple. A thick cotton (denim) rag is dipped in water, then into the grit of sand chosen. It's then rubbed across the surface in a circular motion until the desired effect is achieved. Another tradition is to make a paste of water and sand that is applied with a rag.

Today, sandpapers as well as other commercial abrasives are available to the public. Hand sanding with many of these products can be most rewarding not only in the final outcome of the desired finish of the bronze but also of the patina as well. Once again, 320 grit sandpaper or emery cloth is the finest grit that is needed for the following recipes. Anything finer may only result in the flaking of certain patinas. Hand sanding with these products after mechanically sanding is also recommended, as this will tend to break up any circular patterns left from discs or cones.

When sanding the surface of bronze mechanically or manually, a respirator should always be worn to protect the lungs from harmful dust particles. A face shield, safety glasses, and hand protection is also necessary for this job, especially when mechanically sanding. Long hair should be tied back as a safety precaution. Protective clothing should button at the collar as well as the cuffs. Sanding should also be carried out in a well-ventilated area, as large amounts of airborne particles are created, especially during large projects. Sanding should always be carried out in a different environment than that of patination, as these same particles in the air could become trapped in patina layers or contaminate waxes and other sealers used in the patina process.

SCOTCH-BRITE™ HANDPADS AND STEEL WOOL

After the bronze surface has been mechanically sanded (or to complete a hand sanded project), it is recommended to use Scotch-Brite™ handpads (manufactured by 3M) or any other fine, soapless, oilless scouring pad. Rubbing the surface by hand with these pads will break up and smooth out swirling patterns left from mechanical sanding and will help in the final finish of a job accomplished by hand. The Scotch-Brite™ #96 handpads are recommended for this as, it leaves a fine satin finish that is suitable for many transparent patinas. Scotch-Brite™ #96 handpads are also excellent to use as a highlighting agent in the patina process. They work well in removing liver of sulfur residues from bronze sculpture during the process of a transparent patina. They also work well for burnishing high areas of texture used in more traditional patinas.

Steel wool is the most traditional way of preparing bronze for and during the patina process. It is the last step in either sanding or highlighting if a rich glow to the metal and, consequently, to the patina, is desired. Steel wool comes in a variety of grades. A #1 medium to single "0" are the grades recommended for the patinas explained in this book. Any coarser grade will only scratch the finish, and grades that are finer will tend to leave iron deposits on the surface, which can have unwanted results when coming in contact with patina applications. When purchasing steel wool, always be certain that the wool is oil free. Many producers of steel wool add small amounts of oil both as a fire retardant and to inhibit rusting. These oils can darken and stain the surface of bronze as well as inhibit any chemical reaction during patination.

Bronze or brass wool is always recommended when working with the finishing of bronze. However, it may be difficult to purchase and maintain in stock. These drawbacks are why most patineurs use steel wool.

PUMICE

Pumice is yet another medium used in the final steps of sanding a bronze finish. Placing pumice on a soft rag and rubbing the surface will also create a soft satin glow. Finishing the surface with pumice takes much longer and requires more energy than steel wool. Its use in traditional patinas is best as a burnishing agent. Care should be taken with pumice both in hand sanding and burnishing because its use creates large amounts of dust, which can be destructive to a patina finish and a nuisance to an otherwise somewhat clean environment. Never use pumice around paste waxes, as airborne particles may become mixed with them and may cloud or scratch the patina surface when the contaminated wax is applied.

ORGANIC SOLVENTS

Organic solvents are quite handy when used to clean any oil from chasing and sanding tools as well as natural oils from hands. These oils must be removed or they may inhibit the application of patinas to the surface or produce a spotty effect as the bronze patina ages. Care should always be taken when handling organic solvents. Always wear a respirator rated for "organic vapors." Most of the following solvents may be purchased at hardware and paint supply stores, although very few stores issue Material Safety Data Sheets for these products. Therefore, read all warnings and precautions listed on the solvent container prior to use. The buyer of these solvents takes all responsibilities as to their use, handling, and proper disposal. Never pour organic solvents down the drain as this could have explosive reactions. The concentration of their vapors may be very explosive so organic solvents should be used only with fresh air ventilation or outdoors. All torches, pilot lights, or any other flame should be extinguished before using these products.

Xylene

Xylol (xylene) is one of the most accepted organic solvents used in the final cleansing of the bronze surface preparation for patination. Xylene is an aromatic hydrocarbon that has been known to cause cancer and birth defects in animals and, therefore, caution should always be observed when using this product. As mentioned above, follow all precautions and wear an "organic vapor" rated respirator and safety glasses when using this product. Also, read all precautions on the container prior to opening. The buyer of this solvent takes full responsibility, not only in its use, but also in its proper disposal.

Its cleaning powers are both fast and effective in cleaning oil and grime from the sanded bronze surface. Place a small amount of xylol on a cotton rag or papertowel and gently wipe the surface of the bronze. This cleansing may take two or three treatments in order to remove most contaminates. It will also remove many oil-based Magic Marker™ stains, but will not touch markers that are water-based (only water will remove these). Foreign waxes as well as many paints will be dissolved and removed from the surface.

After the bronze sculpture has been thoroughly cleaned, it must be allowed to sit and dry for a short time in order to let the organic vapors dissipate prior to the patina process.

Isopropyl Alcohol

Isopropyl alcohol is another organic solvent used in cleaning the surface of bronze. It may be purchased in many grocery, hardware, and craft shops as well as pharmacies. Once again, care should be taken when using this product. Read all precautions on its container prior to use. It is used much in the same way as xylol, but does not usually have the same cleansing action as does xylol. It is a weaker solvent and, therefore, is not as fast or efficient as xylol. Under certain conditions, it may leave unwanted residues that may not become apparent until patina chemicals are applied. Therefore, once the bronze surface has been cleaned with isopropyl alcohol, allow time for it to dry and the fumes of the alcohol to dissipate prior to beginning the application of patinas.

Both xylol and isopropyl alcohol must be stored in a fireproof cabinet within the patina studio for obvious reasons listed on their containers. All rags with xylol and Isopropyl alcohol contained in them should be placed in a container outdoors and left to dry. These rags must be kept away from heat and sparks at all times. Once these rags are dry, they should be disposed of according to state and local regulations.

Denatured Alcohol

Denatured alcohol is yet another organic solvent used in the cleaning of bronze surfaces. It is much stronger than isopropyl alcohol and therefore works much better and at a faster rate. Denatured alcohol is great for removing buffing compounds as well as other oil contaminates. Care as to its handling and storage is the same as with xylol and isopropyl alcohol.

CHAPTER SEVEN

7

The Patina Process

This chapter is divided into two major parts: equipment and materials. Since the coloration of bronze requires the use of many strong oxidizers and corrosives, safety is always of prime importance. Safety is a good policy to maintain not only in the area of finishing metal, but in the actual location of the patina process itself. Many tools required in the art of patination have to do with safety. All chemical compounds to be used in the following recipes should come with Material Safety Data Sheets (MSDS), which list not only the unique properties associated with the individual compounds, but also explain the safety requirements associated with the handling of these metal salts. If unfamiliar with any of these compounds, the purchaser and user should always read the Material Safety Data Sheets associated with the compound prior to its handling and use.

EQUIPMENT

Always wear a good respirator when handling, mixing and applying these chemical compounds. Fumes and airborne particles given off by these chemicals can irritate the respiratory system as well as congest the sinuses, which can result in headaches and even nausea in some individuals. There are many different types of respirators available from which to choose. They are all rated for different chemical families. The respirator that is required for use with the following recipes must be rated for "organic vapor/acid gas." Many paint supply stores and most chemical companies will handle this type of respirator. The acid gas rating helps to protect the user from fumes released by the chemical compounds used in these recipes. The organic vapors classification shields against fumes produced by organic sealers as well as xylene, toluene, and other organic solvents. Respirators rated organic vapors/acid gas are not to be used for protection against ammonia or any other ammonium compounds. Respirators for ammonium compounds require different cartridge filters rated for their specific purpose.

Organic vapor/acid gas respirators may be purchased in either half or full mask styles. Half mask designs cover the mouth and nose, while full face masks cover from the top of the forehead to under the chin. Some require a separate purified air supply while others depend on replaceable cartridges for filtration. The most comfortable choice usually is the half mask with replaceable cartridges. Prescription glasses may be worn much more easily if covered either by a safety shield, safety glasses or goggles.

Respirators used for protection during the patina process should be kept clean and functioning properly. Put the mask on tightly but comfortably, placing both hands over the cartridges and breathing in. If air is coming in between the face and respirator, the mask should be tightened to block out contaminated air bypassing the filter cartridges. If fumes are detected while wearing the respirator, cartridges should be replaced. This practice should be routine to every patineur.

Good ventilation is also a strict requirement to remove unwanted fumes from the patina studio unless patinas are applied outdoors; then no ventilation other than a proper respirator is required. There is a wide assortment of ventilation systems available, from large overhead exhaust hoods to wall fans. A combination of both is ideal, but can tend to be somewhat costly. Ensure that the ventilation system chosen for patination is equipped with an explosion-proof exhaust fan. No other will do, especially when applying lacquers and varnishes and working with organic solvents.

Safety glasses or goggles are also necessities for this art. Eyes are the most important tool to a patineur and must be protected at all times around patina applications as well as metal finishing. There is a considerable amount of spattering in patination, not to mention irritating fumes and dust, requiring such protection. Keep the lenses as clean as possible and replace on a regular basis as many chemical compounds will tend to stain plastic lenses. Never wear gas permeable contact lenses while applying patinas as they will become contaminated, irritating the eyes.

Long hair should be tied back out of the path of an ignited torch and should be washed after patina applications as trace elements from the patina process may become trapped in the hair. Wash hands and face thoroughly, as well, after applying patinas.

Good thick rubber gloves are yet another safety tool required for patination. Hands are the second most important tools of the artist of patinas and should be protected while handling and applying chemical compounds used in the following recipes. Chemicals used in this process can be quite irritating and will stain or become embedded in the skin. Most patineurs will have some staining on the hands as this is almost unavoidable, but good protection will minimize this. Always keep an extra pair of gloves on hand, and wash the gloves after use to avoid unwanted contamination either to another patina or to oneself.

Clean, dry, soft oven or kiln mitts are also recommended for handling the hot patinaed bronze after the completion of the patina. Never use synthetic fiber rags to pick up a hot bronze as they will tend to melt to the surface of the hot metal. (Never wear synthetic fiber clothing as a rule while applying patinas as they will tend to melt and stick to the skin if a torch is brought within range.)

Always keep the working area for the patina process as neat and clean as possible. All chemical compounds should be either sealed and/or stored when not in use. Spilled oxides have the potential of contaminating not only other chemical mixtures, but the work area as well. Therefore, all chemical spills, either liquid or crystal/powder, should be cleaned up as soon as possible.

Fire is another hazardous element of the patina process. It is needed to heat and expand the surface of the metal, thereby accepting coloration. The two most common applications of heat are by electric oven or torch. One may be limited by the use of an electric oven as many patterns and "flashing" effects cannot be obtained. Therefore, a hand held torch is highly recommended for the application of patinas. Common sense should be used when working with gas driven torches, whether they be propane, acetylene, natural gas, etc. Propane is the fuel most commonly used in the art of patination. Always ensure that all hose fittings are tight and sealed and that the gas tank is a safe distance from the ignited torch, and never leave an ignited torch unattended. Ensure that gas lines are out of walkways and out from underfoot.

Propane-fed torches used for applying patinas come in a variety of sizes and designs. Most commonly used for average to midsize bronze castings are handheld models with a 1" to 2" diameter orifice tip opening and a pressure control valve either in knob or trigger design to control the size of flame required. Either a straight, open flame or a swirled flame produced by "turbo torches" is recommended. Purchase a handheld torch with a triggering device, if possible, as this will save on the consumption of propane. Tanks used for storage and use of propane come in a variety of sizes, usually sold in "pound" ratings, i.e., 20 pound rating is usually one of the smallest canisters available and is recommended for the novice who wishes to do patinas occasionally. Many patineurs working on the professional level usually use 30, 40, even 100 pound propane tanks when applying patinas.

Always keep the torch used for patinas in good working order and keep the tip free of carbon buildup. As propane is the most dangerous substance used in patinas, any leaks should be dealt with immediately. Torches should be disconnected from their tanks, and tank valves closed tightly and plugged when not in use. Good fire-resistant materials should be used in the structure of tables, working benches, etc. Many patineurs prefer rolling tripods made of steel to handle substantial weight, with a rotating metal grated working surface or turntable. It is always recommended that a patineur lay some sort of fire brick or cinder block over the grated work surface as this will avoid patina contamination transferred from the metal turntable. If a metal tripod or table is not available, then stacking cinder blocks will work.

Running water is necessary for the patina studio, not only as a safety precaution, but also to rinse and neutralize many patinas during their process. Certain chemical compounds used in the following recipes should be rinsed with running water immediately after application on silicon bronze in order to stop their otherwise continuation of oxidation, and also to "set" and brighten many colors.

There is a wide range of water contamination coming out of taps throughout the Americas. Rinsing a hot patinaed bronze with tap water that is alkaline may give quite different results as compared with areas of the western world that use water that is quite acidic, having a low pH reading. High amounts of iron transferred from rusting pipes carried in tap water may green up a light blue patina and should never be used on white patinas as this contamination will tend to turn them yellow or orange. A neutral pH reading (pH 7) is best for rinsing, as little change occurs. The advantage to having unusual chemical combinations suspended in tap water is that it gives uniqueness to certain patinas not achieved anywhere else on the continent.

MATERIALS

Highlighting Agents

Products used in the patina process for burnishing textured areas by means of removing or "releasing" base coats are termed highlighting agents. The idea of this process is to bring texture to the forefront and/or give depth to transparent patinas. Abrasive handpads made of a synthetic mesh such as 3M Scotch-Brite™ #96 and #86 handpads are ideal for this purpose. The #96 Scotch-Brite™ handpads are used to highlight where sharp contrast is required between high and recessed areas of a textured surface. On the other hand, using #86 Scotch-Brite™ handpads will soften this contrast, removing the base coat in recessed areas as well. The great advantage of using these modern abrasive handpads is that there is no foreign metal contamination deposited on the bronze surface, as is possible with the use of steel wool pads.

Steel wool is the most traditional product used in the highlighting process. Ensure that steel wool to be used for highlighting bronze is free of oil as this will contaminate the bronze surface, thus inhibiting chemical coloration. The recommended abrasive grades used for the following recipes range from single "0" to #1 medium grade. Any grade higher, such as #2 medium, will tend to scratch the surface, and grades finer than single "0" may leave unseen and unwanted iron deposits on the surface, which may interfere in the achievement of particular colors desired. Steel wool is also recommended to soften and even brighten a surface highlighted previously with Scotch-Brite™ handpads. The result is more of a satin glow, softening scratches on the surface produced by using Scotch-Brite™ handpads. Steel wool may also be used independently as a highlighting agent if a soft, darker effect is desired.

Always rinse the bronze surface frequently and thoroughly when using steel wool as rust deposits may develop quickly from remaining particles of wool. If the patineur is lucky enough to have purchased brass wool instead, this problem is eliminated.

Brass brushes are also handy in the highlighting process for scratch-brushing base coats as well as giving an untreated bronze a satin finish. Brass brushes are handy in removing base coat deposits from deep crevices around noses and eyes found in representational sculpture. They are also used in giving a lighter effect to heavily textured surfaces. Steel brushes are not recommended for this process as, once again, they will tend to leave iron contaminates on the bronze surface that may interfere with the patina process.

Silica sand is yet another medium used for highlighting bronze. Placing sand on a damp rag and rubbing the surface will tend to leave a subdued contrast between high and low recessed textures. This medium may also be used to buff or burnish areas of the bronze surface after the patina is applied, to indicate years of wear.

Pumice and rotten stone are highlighting agents that may be used to "antique" a bronze surface when used dry. A slurry mixture of pumice can be used to highlight base coats as well. Pumice should never be used dry in the wet removal of base coats, as it tends to "cake" and repel water when the patineur attempts to rinse and remove such mediums. Pumice is much more abrasive than rotten stone, and thus care should be taken when burnishing certain areas of the patinaed surface. Rotten stone is a medium used more to achieve a dusty finish on the bronze patina. It may be mixed with clear waxes to accomplish the same end results. Both pumice and rotten stone are usually applied with a soft rag in a circular motion, using little pressure. Rotten stone may also be used on a rag to help in the polishing of waxes as this may produce an almost glass finish.

Chemical Compounds

The use of chemical compounds in combination with heat is what is required to achieve coloration on bronze in the following recipes. There are basically three categories of inorganic metal salts used within these instructions serving distinct functions, either applied individually or combined in mixtures. In the following recipes, polysulfides are used for base coats, nitrates function as binders, and oxides as well as hydroxides are used to accent the coloration brought about by nitrate binders.

Safety measures should always be observed when handling and applying the following chemical compounds. As mentioned previously, read all information regarding chemical hazards and Material Safety Data Sheets prior to their use. Remember that wearing a good organic vapor/acid gas rated respirator, safety glasses or goggles, and rubber gloves with a rubber apron are needed in the handling and application of these chemical compounds to the surface of bronze. Never smoke, eat, or drink around these compounds as bodily contamination may result.

Coloration from the following compounds is achieved easily and with lasting results when applied and sealed correctly on silicon bronze. Certain compounds used on other bronze alloys may not be suitable for silicon bronze as they will tend to "sluff" and/or darken on Everdur, attesting to their unstable properties. Chlorides are a family of metal salts that should never be used to patina silicon bronze professionally for this reason, as well as because of their ability to having damaging results.

Nearly all the published recipes for greens call for chlorides, but according to Fink and Eldridge, the use of ammoniac (ammonium chloride), hydrochloric acid, or any other chloride is to be condemned because chlorides induce 'bronze disease,' a malignant form of corrosion which spreads rapidly and has a destructive effect.[7]

Any conservationist who deals with bronze can attest to this. However, for non-professional applications, experimenting with chlorides can be fun, giving powdery, bright, aging effects to the surface. Chlorides are usually used in the field of cold patina processes which, in most cases, are quite unstable on the surface of silicon bronze and do not have the biting efficiently as do hot patina applications requiring nitrate salts.

There are quality grades of chemical compounds, i.e., analytical reagent, U.S.P., and technical grades. Analytical reagent grade is the purest form of any chemical compound that may be purchased. It is always recommended that the patineur purchase reagent grade nitrates in the following recipes. However, this can be costly to the user, as compared with using technical grades, which are not as pure in compound structure. When purchasing the following nitrates, always ask if they are available in a reagent grade and check the price. If it is within budget, then use reagent grade. This grade may give excellent results the first time. For example, white patinas tend to stay whiter and do not green or yellow as rapidly using reagent grade bismuth nitrate as opposed to using a technical grade. The professional patineur usually works with both grades, but for the novice or apprentice, to avoid possible frustrations when applying the following nitrates, analytical reagent grades have many advantages.

U.S.P. grades are those that meet specifications for use as pharmaceuticals. Not as expensive as reagent grade normally, U.S.P. grades still tend to be of superb quality. There is only one chemical used in the following recipes that is rated for pharmaceuticals, and that is sulfurated potash. Always buy and use U.S.P. grade potassium sulfide as it suspends better and longer in water and tends to coat the surface of the bronze better than technical grades.

Technical grades of the following compounds may be used when reagent grades are unavailable. They are not as purified as reagent grades and, therefore, tend to be much cheaper. This is especially the case when purchasing nitrates. But as mentioned before, technical grades may be more frustrating for the beginner to work with than reagent grades. Oxides used in the following recipes are almost always purchased in a technical grade. Their use is strictly for color, which is permanent in pure inorganic forms as opposed to synthetic ones.

On the following page is a list of the chemical compounds used, their grade preference, and unique coloration properties.

Chemical Compounds	*Grade*	*Color Range*
Water	Distilled/tap	
Sulfurated Potash	U.S.P.	Gray, black
Ammonium Sulfide	Tech.	Blue-gray, black
Birchwood Casey™ M20	Premixed	Brown, gray, black
Cupric Nitrate	A.R./tech.	Blue, green
Ferric Nitrate	A.R./tech.	Yellow, gold, brown, red, burgundy
Bismuth Nitrate	A.R./tech.	White, cream, gray
Zinc Nitrate	A.R./tech.	White, grays
Silver Nitrate	A.R./tech.	Silver, cream, gray
Potassium Dichromate	A.R./tech.	Ambers, orange
Sodium Thiosulfate	A.R./tech.	Metallic binder
Ferric Oxide Fe_2O_3	Tech.	Red, rust
Ferric Oxide Black Fe_3O_4	Tech.	Black
Chromium Oxide	Tech.	Green
Titanium Oxide (dioxide)	Tech.	White
Stannic Oxide	Tech.	White

All of the above compounds should be sealed tightly in appropriate, well-labeled, glass or plastic containers and stored in a cool, dry place.

Water H_2O

Water is the true foundation for all patinas, whether hot or cold, in that this medium is used to suspend and transfer chemical compounds to the bronze surface, thus achieving coloration. Unless water with a neutral pH is available, using distilled water is advisable when mixing the following compounds. Trace elements in water that are either too alkaline or acidic may give unpredictable results in the patina application, which can be most frustrating. However, rinsing patinas with distilled water may not be cost effective and is usually unnecessary. All of the chemical compounds used in the following recipes were suspended in distilled water and then neutralized, when needed, with tap water of a pH 7 rating.

BASE COATS

Sulfurated Potash (Potassium Sulfide) K_2S

Potassium sulfide, or "liver of sulfur," is the most common chemical compound used in the coloration of bronze, achieving colors ranging from yellow to brown to gray-black, depending on its concentration within a water suspension. This compound is most commonly sold under the name of sulfurated potash, and it usually comes in yellow chips or lumps, depending on the manufacturer. Purchasing U.S.P. grade is recommended for use in the following recipes. It reacts by "oxidizing" the element of copper found in the bronze alloy, leaving dark residues that may either be highlighted or brushed from the surface, giving the patina a quality of depth.

Using U.S.P. grade potassium sulfide is recommended as it gives a nice, even coloration to the bronze surface as opposed to a technical grade, which can react unevenly, resulting in a blotchy, uneven appearance.

Polysulfides such as liver of sulfur are the only compounds applied to a cold bronze surface in the following hot patina applications. When the surface of the bronze is heated, the molecular structure is expanded, possibly opening porous areas of the casting. If potash is applied to a hot metal surface, it may become trapped in these porous areas, only to leach out as white specks in clusters on the patinaed surface, which not only disturbs the effect of the patina but also draws attention to a poor casting. Applying potassium sulfide to a hot casting can also make the highlighting process more difficult. Therefore, unless otherwise suggested, liver of sulfur is applied cold in the following recipes.

Most patineurs will make a concentrated mixture of liver of sulfur and then dilute it as needed for specific color values required. Many patineurs also mix only enough of this solution as will be used in a day, because sulfurated potash dissolved in water tends to have a short shelf life. However, the author has found that U.S.P. grade sulfurated potash suspended in distilled water or tap water with a pH 7 rating may last up to three weeks when kept tightly sealed. This is quite handy for those patineurs working in a high production setting where mixing small amounts of liver of sulfur may be a waste of valuable time. For a concentrated mixture of liver of sulfur, add approximately one lump, about the size of a quarter, to one quart of water. Let this solution set until these yellow lumps are completely dissolved. Dilution of this concentration depends on the desired effect. For the following recipes, a dark gray is desired; therefore, mix four tablespoons of concentrate to one pint of water. This is then either sprayed, brushed, or poured over the bronze surface. Smaller bronzes may even be dipped in this solution to achieve a dark gray required for base coats. The surface of the bronze should go through many quick color changes, from gold to purplish white and then onto dark gray. If this process happens too fast, the base coat of copper oxides may tend to flake off later, and streaks may become etched deeply into the bronze, making the task of highlighting more difficult. If the bronze turns black immediately while applying liver of sulfur, the solution is too strong and should be diluted.

In the following recipes, liver of sulfur has been sprayed on the bronze surface rather than brushed on or dipped. Plastic squirt bottles are convenient for this application on small to medium size bronzes. Larger commercial sprayers, like those used in the broadcasting of herbicides or pesticides, may be used to spray larger monumental size pieces. Rinsing with water is a must after applying this sulfide to the bronze surface for this dilutes and stops any further reaction of this compound to the metal. If highlighting or rubbing back the sulfide residues is required, rinsing with water is also recommended, usually as one continues highlighting.

When using a sprayer, whether it be squirt bottle or spray tank, it is necessary to continually mist the bronze evenly until a dark gray appears. Then concentrate on the areas that may be slower to change, until a nice even coat is attained. Rinse and either highlight where required or continue on, using liver of sulfur as a base coat.

Liver of sulfur can be highlighted quite easily on cold bronze by using 3M Scotch-Brite™ abrasive pads, steel wool, sand and/or brass brushes to remove sulfide residues from the bronze surface. Each highlighting agent will give the bronze base coat a different appearance. Experiment with all of these to further understand their use in achieving a wide range of effects.

Highlighting liver of sulfur on a hot bronze can give a beautiful steel gray to the surface, making for a rich, yet reflective base coat.

Ammonium Sulfide $(NH_4)_2S$

Another polysulfide used for achieving a dark base coat is ammonium sulfide. Its basic coloration on bronze seems similar to that of potassium sulfide or liver of sulfur. However, where liver of sulfur gives more of brown to purplish black, ammonium sulfide leaves more of a blue-black residue. Highlighting ammonium sulfide is similar to that of liver of sulfur.

Ammonium sulfide, though somewhat unstable, has a far wider range of colors and effects than liver of sulfur. Weak solutions may be spattered onto the warm surface of bronze and then "heat flashed" with a torch to achieve silvery patterns. Yellow and even dark blues can be acquired but are very unstable on silicon bronze and tend to turn dark brown to black in a short time. One disadvantage to using ammonium sulfide is that it is difficult to control, changing patinas rapidly in some cases, from light brown to black.

Ammonium sulfide comes in a liquid state, which gives it yet another disadvantage, especially where shipping is concerned. Many chemical companies choose not to handle ammonium sulfide because of the concerns associated with shipping. For these reasons, ammonium sulfide was not used on any of the following plates. However, this compound is used as a liver substitute in some of the recipes and as alternative effects in others.

Birchwood Casey™ M20

Birchwood Casey laboratories have been in the business of gun bluing for years. They have expanded over time to include darkening or antiquing solutions in browns and blacks for various metals. M20 antique black is produced for its etching ability on bronze and brass. Birchwood Casey™ antique black is acidic and therefore reacts much differently on the bronze surface than does its alkaline counterpart, liver of sulfur, but with similar results. Antique black comes in a liquid state and should be diluted 50% with water when applied to silicon bronze. This solution can either be sprayed or brushed on the surface, achieving a dark brown black residual on a cold surface. It can be highlighted as easily as liver of sulfur. To be used as an opaque base coat for further chemical layers, an M20 50-50 solution is either sprayed or brushed onto the cool bronze surface until an even brownish-black is achieved. The bronze is then rinsed and heated until hot, and the surface is then polished back with steel wool, which leaves a rich gray-black lustrous finish. Then subsequent layers may be added. *Or, before heating the bronze, use a metal or plastic bristle scrub brush and while rinsing, remove the brownish black residual, thus leaving a similar effect.*

As a base coat, Birchwood Casey™ tends to be much more stable for silicon bronze than liver of sulfur; therefore, it is highly recommended for outdoor use on monuments to be placed in environments that would otherwise be damaging to bronze patinas. Do not experiment by mixing Birchwood Casey™ antique black with other compounds. M20 is a premixed solution; tampering or interfering with its chemical combination by the addition of other compounds can delete its ability to color bronze. It can also be quite dangerous to introduce foreign compounds into the Birchwood Casey™ premixed solution as violent reactions may occur releasing toxic gases.

This product may be purchased directly form Birchwood Casey Laboratories in Eden Prairie, Minnesota, or it may be handled in smaller quantities by arts and craft shops.

NITRATES NO_3

The following chemicals listed are of the nitrate family, which are metal salts of nitric acid. These salts which are used to achieve true color (ferric nitrate, bismuth nitrate, silver nitrate, and zinc nitrate) are used in the following recipes for color and as a binder for oxides.

Achieving specific colors may take time and practice in the art of hot patina applications, for these nitrates are considered to be heat sensitive, prone to fading, scorching, etc. Care should always be observed when handling and applying these chemicals as they are quite corrosive and toxic to the human body, causing possible damage to the lungs, liver, and kidneys. These nitrates can be transmitted by breathing in fumes and can be absorbed through the skin. Always refer to the hazards chapter pertaining to a specific chemical prior to its use.

Each nitrate has specific characteristics which make it unique. Besides color, some nitrates are better binders than others, some are more transparent, while others are completely opaque. Some nitrates give the idea of depth while others function to block out this illusion.

The following nitrates are mixed individually or together in distilled water as an abnormal mineral content in tap water may interfere with specific coloration desired. However, most, but not all, of the nitrate applications in the following recipes are rinsed with neutral pH 7 rated tap water. This is necessary in order to stop and neutralize the acidity of the nitrate "biting" action. It is also used to "set" and brighten nitrate patinas.

Basic rules of suspending nitrates in water, whether mixed or individually, are always to pour these nitrate crystals into water, and always to start with a week solution. It can always be strengthened as needed by adding more crystals.

As nitrate patinas age on the surface of bronze, they tend to darken and take on mellow, more subdued tones of coloration. This is seen mostly on traditional patinas found on more antique bronzes. This is a natural process, but with correct application and upkeep, this process may be slowed considerably, giving the patina many years of life.

Cupric Nitrate $CuNO_3$

Cupric nitrate is one of the oldest chemical compounds on the patina palette. Historically, it was used in a thick mixture as a base coat for low copper bronze containing foreign metals such as brass and zinc rod, used to fill cavities on poorly cast surfaces. As a result, cupric nitrate is compatible with many other chemical compounds used. These blue crystals give a color range from sky blue to a green turquoise when applied to a hot surface. Cupric nitrate can be used to create the illusion of transparency or function as a great opaque patina, giving the look of age and elegance.

Cupric nitrate is heat sensitive, as mentioned earlier. This can be frustrating when trying to achieve an even valued coat, or it can be exciting when flame flashed, creating a multitude of colors. This, however, is difficult to control and is a very unstable patina, especially on silicon bronze.

Cupric nitrate tends to be stable on most bronzes except for Everdur 95-4-1. This is because of the high amount of copper used in this most popular bronze. Cupric nitrate on silicon bronze may, with time, develop large red to raw sienna colored patches in the patina. It is believed to be a reduction process creating dicuprus oxides, which are the reddish colors observed in an otherwise blue or green patina. Dicuprous oxides can develop as a result of placing high copper salts on the surface of copper or on an alloy of high copper content. To slow or even stop this action, a good neutral base coat is required. For the novice or apprentice, liver of sulfur will suffice, but this is never recommended on the professional level as a base coat for cupric nitrate, because liver of sulfur tends to speed up the process of chemical reduction. There are many patineurs now who are using different and unusual base coats, achieving excellent results. Most widely used of these is Birchwood Casey™ M20. Another base coat used quite often is a hot application of ferric nitrate and sodium thiosulfate. This later base coat tends to give a green coloration to the cupric as it ages. If blue is desired, use antique black M20 instead. Care should still be taken when choosing cupric nitrate for use outdoors as nothing so far is 100% reduction proof. In order to avoid dicuprous oxide development, the author recommends mixing Zinc Nitrate into cupric solutions at a ratio of 1 to 2.

Ferric Nitrate $FeNO_3$

If only one chemical can be purchased for bronze patinas, it should be ferric nitrate. Yellow, gold, orange, various shades of brown, red, and burgundy are all colors produced by ferric nitrate. These individual colors are achieved by chemical strength in combination with varying degrees of temperature. A weak solution of ferric nitrate produces yellow and gold, but by applying more heat and more layers of this weak mixture, browns and even reds may be developed. On the other hand, if a stronger solution of ferric nitrate is applied to bronze, dark browns, reds, and burgundies will be the end result.

Crystals of ferric nitrate are a clear, light lavender color that, when added to water, change color very little. This nitrate is also one of the oldest compounds on the patina palette and is used predominantly in the western world. It is compatible with most of the other chemicals used, both nitrates and oxides. It is the only transparent nitrate used, but in strong concentration it can be quite opaque. In the majority of the following recipes, ferric nitrate is used as a translucent overlay or hot undercoat. It is also used independently or mixed with other nitrates and/or oxides to give rich opaqueness to a patinaed surface. Experimentation with this chemical is not only fun, but can be exciting, giving the widest range of coloration of any of the nitrates listed. Mixed with or laid over other nitrates, it has almost infinite possibilities.

Many foundries and independent patineurs over the centuries have made at least one of the nitrates used for patination. These secret recipes became their individual trademarks. Homemade versions of, say, cupric nitrate and ferric nitrate, have been used for centuries by many foundries in Europe as well as many parts of Asia, and are now used more in the Americas. The dangerous process of making metal nitrates is best left up to the master patineur as the procedure of nitrate fabrication requires the use of nitric acid 70%, which is a strong corrosive. Extreme care must be observed, and safety protection must be worn at all times while handling this acid.

This process is executed outdoors and far away from people, animals, and natural running water. For ferric nitrate, a handful of iron nails (8P common box) are placed in the bottom of a Pyrex™ coffee pot or any Pyrex™ jar. Pyrex™ or some other heat resistant glassware is required as great amounts of heat are given off by the following chemical reaction. The nails are just covered with water—1/2 to 2/3 cup. Then 1/2 to 2/3 cup of nitric acid is poured into the water-covered nails. This action must be done swiftly, and one must evacuate the area immediately as poisonous gases are given off (seen as a bright orange to deep red ominous cloud). It dissipates within seconds. Wait two to five minutes, or until the boiling from the chemical reaction has subsided, and then fill the container with hot water. This will easily make a liter to a half gallon of concentrated liquid ferric nitrate. It must be strained and diluted when used for patination. As mentioned before, this procedure is not recommended for the novice or apprentice as it is quite dangerous. The master patineur is the best person for this task.

As also mentioned before, many patineurs in the Americas use homemade ferric nitrate; therefore, many of the recipes will give measurements for both homemade and reagent grade ferric nitrate.

Please keep in mind, if it isn't an absolute necessity to make homemade versions of nitrates, then by all means don't. We humans pollute so much into the atmosphere that there is no need to add to it if there are other alternatives.

Ferric nitrate is also the only nitrate used where rinsing is not required after application as this will cause the patina to sluff, fade, and flake off.

Bismuth Nitrate $BiNO_3$

Bismuth nitrate is used in the patina process to achieve dusty, matte, whitish grays as well as opaque white effects. Many patineurs misunderstand the effects and use of bismuth nitrate. Bismuth nitrate comes in the form of transparent, colorless crystals that have a nitric odor. It also never quite dissolves in water, so the solution should be shaken or stirred occasionally to suspend the bismuth. This inability to decompose rapidly has advantages in achieving many different effects in pattern as well as color. When freshly mixed, transparent dusty effects can occur, or marbling over other compounds may result. If white is required, the water-bismuth solution should be left to soak for a few days along with the addition of certain oxides.

Many other colors can be achieved using bismuth nitrate in combination with other oxides.

For example, mixing bismuth nitrate with chromium oxide can give light, dusty pea green, or using bismuth nitrate with a few crystals of "hematite" red ferric oxide can achieve pink results. More details will be given to this process in the recipes. However, this gives an idea of how diverse this basic compound is.

Bismuth nitrate is also excellent in changing the color value of other nitrates. By using bismuth with cupric nitrate, one may achieve a whitish-blue coloration. Mixing bismuth with ferric nitrate may tend to lighten the effect from reds to more opaque oranges, ochre, and even yellow. Practice is essential in this; however, these colors may be achieved with time and practice.

Bismuth nitrate should usually be rinsed after application to a bronze surface. This will neutralize any reactive chemical activity as well as cause the true chalky, antique look to appear for which bismuth nitrate is so well known.

Zinc Nitrate $ZnNO_3$

Zinc nitrate used traditionally on brass gives a white to cream white patina to bronze. It must be applied to the bronze surface at much hotter temperatures than any other nitrate mentioned. Depending on the desired effect, zinc nitrate may be brushed or sprayed on the surface. It also mixes well with other nitrates and oxides.

Care should be taken when dealing with zinc nitrate. It comes in a clear crystalline form and, when mixed with water, the solution stays crystal clear. Unlike the other nitrates, one may not detect that he or she is inhaling zinc fumes until zinc poisoning occurs. The feeling is similar to that of having the flu. A good respirator and rubber gloves are essential.

Zinc nitrate also scorches quite easily if the bronze surface is not hot enough. Practice is required when dealing with this nitrate. The author recommends adding Zinc Nitrate crystals to cupric nitrate crystals at a ratio of 1 to 2 to help avoid dicuprous oxide development (see page 47 under Cupric nitrate).

Silver Nitrate $AgNO_3$

The most exquisite contemporary effects can be accomplished using silver nitrate. Yet it can be used very tastefully in accenting traditional patinas. Silver nitrate is a light and heat sensitive compound, which gives it both advantages and disadvantages. It is easily scorched, both in weak and concentrated mixtures. However, flashing a weak solution applied to the surface of the bronze can give a metallic sparkle and gleam seen in a multitude of patterns. Applied in stronger concentrations, silver nitrate is capable of producing cream white, beiges, and, by burnishing with single "0" steel wool, will produce a look of silver plating.

Silver nitrate is usually purchased in a clear translucent crystal form for patination, and a little goes a long way. This is good since silver nitrate is the most expensive nitrate on the patina palette. Its biting ability is deeper than any other nitrate used. It also mixes well with other nitrates for a variety of results.

Silver nitrate is quite poisonous, so special care should be observed when handling and applying this compound. Its ability to stain skin is phenomenal, so rubber gloves should always be worn. Fumes given off by this chemical are quite toxic, so good ventilation is an absolute. If applying silver nitrate outdoors, ensure that this procedure is done out of direct sunlight as this will darken the nitrate solution, which will transfer to the bronze surface, resulting in more of a pewter or lead look than one of silver.

A smooth 320 finish is required for bright silver patterns, and solid effects. Reflection is everything to the brightness of metal; the smoother and brighter the bronze, the same it will be with the silver. Attempting to apply silver nitrate to polished bronze surfaces may only result in cracking and flaking, as with most patinas on polished surfaces. On a blasted surface, silver nitrate can give gray effects resembling lead or gray steel when single "0" steel wool is used.

OXIDES

Metal oxides are the family of compounds used in bronze patination that, when mixed with nitrates, expand considerably the hue and value choices of color used on the bronze surface. Also, when used as washes, they give depth and age to a patina. The "dusty" look is achieved easily when oxides are used in the form of oxide washes. Oxides are also used to make patinas appear more opaque; i.e., mixing titanium oxide with ferric nitrate will give an opaque appearance to an otherwise translucent patina. Oxides, as a whole, are not as hazardous as the nitrate or sulfide families. The dust given off when using these compounds can be a different problem, however. Many metal oxides are considered "nuisance particulates," meaning they may be easily and unknowingly dispersed throughout the working environment, contaminating brushes, other chemical solutions left unprotected, waxes, etc. Therefore, they should be used with care and control.

Oxides must always be accompanied with a nitrate binder, either in mixture or sandwiched between nitrate layers as in oxide washes. Using nitrates alone will not work as they have no binding power of their own and tend to rub off the bronze surface quite easily.

Ferric Oxide (Hematite) Fe_2O_3

The ferric oxide family is a category of fine powders that comes in a wide range of colors—from dark reds and rust to bright yellow. These oxides are the basic pigments used in many acrylic and oil paints, giving rise to such colors as burnt umber, raw sienna, oxide yellow, etc. The ferric oxide red that is used in the following recipes is labeled "hematite" or blood red. This fine red powder is, for most purposes, non toxic. However, the dust given off during a patina project may irritate the respiratory system, so a good respirator is recommended. By mixing hematite red with ferric nitrate, a true rich red may appear. By mixing titanium oxide with hematite and bismuth, hot pinks may be achieved. Mauve opaques are yet another range that may be attained using hematite red.

Ferric Oxide (Black) Fe_3O_4

This oxide (ferreso ferric oxide) is a synthetically produced pigment which is used for blacks or black accents. Mixing ferrric oxide black with ferric nitrate can give variations from black to red black, brown black, etc. It may also be stippled over an existing patina in a marbling fashion. Mixing ferreso ferric oxide with titanium oxide and bismuth nitrate (as a binder) gives a full range of opaque grays. As a wash, it may even be used to "antique" an exciting patina.

Non-toxic except when taken internally, this compound has quite the versatility in the field of patination. Ferreso ferric oxide is also used extensively in the following recipes; it is even used as a substitute for liver of sulfur in a few. Therefore, this is a must for the patineur's palette.

Chromium Oxide Cr_2O_3

Chromium oxide is used for greens. Its green value is quite intense, and a little goes a long way. "Kelly green" or "royal green" in appearance, it can be mixed with titanium oxide in order achieve many tints within the green spectrum. Chromium oxide is a carcinogen and, therefore, must be handled with care, using sufficient protection. It is excellent for green washes, or it may be placed on the surface of a hot bronze in order to achieve many interesting effects, such as aging a French brown patina or warming a cool cupric nitrate appearance.

As with all oxides, in order to spray or spatter chromium oxide through squirt bottles or air brushes, chromium oxide must have time to soak first within a nitrate solution. This soaking may take a few days. So, if squirting or spattering is required to achieve a certain effect, ensure that the color solution of oxides and nitrates have been soaking for some time. If this procedure is not carried out prior to spraying, oxide powders will tend to clog a spray orifice, stopping any further spray action. Also, when spraying, make sure that the solution is continuously stirred or agitated as oxides will tend to settle out of oxide-nitrate solutions.

Titanium Oxide (Titanium Dioxide) TiO_2

Probably the most abundantly used pigment in the western world is titanium oxide. This white pigment is used in most house paints, plastics, etc. It is almost impossible to avoid being exposed to its presence. As mentioned, titanium oxide is used when white or chalky effects are required. Mixing titanium oxide with bismuth nitrate can be placed on a hot bronze surface in order to achieve a completely white finish or patterns of a lacy fashion. It can be mixed with ferric nitrate to give rise to a rich, dusty opaque brown. Titanium oxide's use as an oxide wash is probably more popular than any other oxide wash. The various applications mentioned above are but a few that are available and will be discussed in the recipes.

Stannic Oxide (Tin Oxide) SnO_2

Stannic oxide is used as a substitute for titanium oxide for whites. It may also be mixed with titanium oxide and bismuth nitrate to ensure an absolute white. Being much more expensive than any other oxide, stannic oxide is not used as readily as titanium, and, therefore, its use is fairly unknown until recently. Its use for coloration in the art of patination has a much longer history than that of titanium oxide, but, as mentioned before, because of its extreme cost, titanium oxide has replaced its use. Therefore, stannic oxide is only used in the following recipes as an alternative to titanium oxide or in combination with it.

ASSORTED COMPOUNDS

Potassium Dichromate $K_2Cr_2O_7$

Potassium dichromate is another compound of versatility. Like ferric nitrate, it makes a good transparent patina for amber and oranges. Its use as an overlay, or in mixture with cupric nitrate, results in opaque, bright yellow to mustard ochres. Although a standard on the red brass patina palette, it is a bit unstable on silicon bronze, and it is only mentioned as an alternative to ferric nitrate in some of the variations listed.

Potassium dichromate is a listed carcinogen and, therefore, it should always be handled with care. For best results, apply potassium dichromate to a smooth or textured surface that has been scrubbed by brass brushes. The look of an antique golden amber or honey color is then easily attained. It mixes well with some compounds and not so well with others. Therefore, for the following recipes, only use potassium dichromate where mentioned.

Sodium Thiosulfate $Na_2S_2O_3$

Sodium thiosulfate is used in combination with ferric nitrate to give more of a bite to the patina as well as give the finish more of a metallic appearance. Sodium thiosulfate comes in a clear crystal. Only three or four large crystals are needed in a ferric nitrate/water solution to increase its binding power. On a sanded surface, it is essential in achieving an iridescent, warm copper look. Ten to twelve or more crystals will tend to give more of an opaque, classic look to ferric nitrate when applied to hot bronze. Sodium is sensitive to flame heat, so care must be taken as not to easily scorch the patina.

Commercial Pigments

Dry paint pigments in many cases are nothing more than finely ground inorganic oxides, i.e., titanium, chromium, and many variations of iron oxide. They may be used as substitution for many of the coarse oxides purchased and used for patination, but with care. Because they are so finely ground, a little goes a long way and once bound to the surface, does not shift or wash as easily as the coarse oxides.

There are many advantages to using other paint pigments as well for many of the colors, such as Prussian blue (which is ferriferro cyanide). When used in combination with cupric nitrate and then rinsed , they can give iridescent light blues and deep midnight shades.

Many pigments do not become suspended in the nitrate solutions listed. Therefore, always place pigments on an individual dry palette, then dab a brush carrying a nitrate solution into the pigment. Very little pigment is used. Apply it in an almost limitless field of color, pattern, contrast, warmth, and compatibility.

Many people unfamiliar with the history of the art of patination tend to disapprove of the use of pigments, not realizing that many of these pigments are actually chemical compounds that have been used in patina recipes for centuries. Many of these compounds are no longer readily available to the public for use other than by way of pigments. Zinc white pigment, for example, is pure zinc oxide and was used as an oxide for whites centuries before the use of titanium.

Patinas all over the world incorporate dry pigments to subdue, accent, and/or warm most nitrates used. Dry pigments are also used to transfer coloration in a wax medium. This adds final color and depth to the patina.

Metal Powders

Metal powders composed of gold, bronze, silver, or aluminum are all available for use with nitrates and oxides to give a glimmer or sparkle to a patina. Used very little in this country, it has been observed in use by many patineurs around the world. Not very popular because of its fragile finish, patinas incorporating metal powders should be well sealed with a sprayed lacquer prior to handling. Plate #147 is a good example of using either gold or bronze powder with ferric nitrate as a binder and base coat. No contemporary patina palette is complete without the presence of these powders. They also transfer well in caseins, to give a glittery finish to a patina.

SEALERS

Many patinas require protection from the environment in order to maintain pattern and coloration. As all patinas age, they become darker. A good protective coat will slow this process by many years. Patinas on silicon bronze darken quicker and/or change more rapidly than on other bronze alloys used for casting sculpture.

Applying waxes to a hot or cold surface is most traditional, but is unsuitable as the only coat of protection for many patinas on Everdur 95-4-1. European patineurs have been using varnishes and lacquers for over 200 years with great success. Many would suspend pigments in coatings of varnishes or lacquers in order to warm or soften a particular color. These pigmented varnishes and lacquers were also used to attain the effect of a transparent patina. Waxes were usually applied over these hard finishes in order to soften their high reflective glare and enrich the final result. Hard sealers, such as varnishes and lacquers, come in a variety of mixtures. Make sure that hard sealers chosen are those made for use on metal, not wood. The buyer of these products will have to experiment with each type and brand, as some will darken a patina while others will change the coloration very little, if at all.

There are other sealers produced for sealing "specific" metals. One such sealer is labeled Incralac™, which was developed by the "International Copper Research Association" and is manufactured in the Untied States by Stan Chem in East Berlin, Connecticut. Incralac™ is a clear acrylic lacquer suspended in three solvents: toluol, xylol, and methyl ethyl ketone. On the positive side, Incralac's acrylic nature gives with the expansion and contraction of outdoor bronzes for many years, if applied correctly. This depends, of course, on the environmental quality of the bronze. It dries quickly and changes patinas, in most cases, very little. Incralac™ may be brushed or sprayed onto the surface of bronze in diluted form—50-50 dilute with xylol or toloul. Many of the following patina plates are sealed with Incralac™ by means of airbrushing one thin coat. To be used on bronzes that are to be placed outdoors, two or three coats are required. Incralac™ must always be placed on clean patinaed surfaces, void of wax, as this will inhibit this lacquer's protective bonding with the bronze. A flattening paste is also manufactured to be used with Incralac™, helping to eliminate its otherwise high glossy "plastic appearance."

The downside of Incralac™ is the safety health hazard associated with this lacquer. Like most lacquers, it is quite flammable, and all torches or any open flame must be extinguished prior to its use. The fumes given off while applying Incralac are quite toxic and explosive. Good ventilation is a must. If used indoors, an applicable ventilation system is required including an explosion-proof fan. A respirator rated for organic vapors/acid gas must also be worn while handling this product. Incralac™ and its thinners should always be stored in fireproof cabinets when not in use.

Other alternatives to hard sealers are traditional waxes or "soft sealers," applied to a hot or cold patinaed surface. Wax coatings have been used for over 2000 years on metals to inhibit oxidation and preserve finishes. Waxes do not have the sealing power, in many cases, as do lacquers especially, and therefore patinas tend to change at a more rapid pace, especially on those bronzes that are handled considerably.

For hot waxing, Johnson's Paste Wax™ is recommended, as this synthetic wax goes on smooth and, if not over applied, can be buffed to a smooth glossy finish.

Clear waxes that are applied to a cold surface, over a fresh patina or Incralac™ finish, are usually composed of carnauba wax, which is a natural wax extracted from palm trees or beeswax. Carnauba wax is an extremely hard wax that gives a beautiful deep luster when buffed with a soft rag. Beeswax gives similar results, but beeswax tends to be somewhat softer than carnauba wax.

Carnauba wax and beeswax are sold in chunks, bricks, or crystals. These must be dissolved in turpentine prior to application, then applied sparingly to the surface with a soft brush. Never apply any waxes to a patina with a rag as this will tend to shift and "press" certain patterns and textures. After the wax has dried, then a soft rag is used to buff the finished surface.

This process of mixing waxes for sealing bronze is definitely one for experimentation but is unnecessary since they are now sold premixed in paste form, ready to use. The most popular in the Americas for sealing patinaed bronze is Trewax™. This wax is manufactured by Chemifax and is sold in many hardware stores. Trewax™ is a carnauba-based wax that is purchased either in clear or pigmented forms. Clear wax is always recommended for patination; however, pigmented carnauba wax can achieve warmer colors to a chemical patina, and so experimentation is a must. Applied over Incralac™, Trewax™ will attain a softer glow, toning the plastic glow that may result from the Incralac™. Trewax™ also tends to dry at a much faster rate than other waxes, changing the coloration of the patina very little, if at all.

Other waxes used in the art of patination are functional pigmented waxes, such as shoe polishes in wax form, and floor waxes. In many Italian as well as Thai and Indonesian foundries, colored floor waxes are used as they are quite durable and give an extra richness to a patinaed finish. They are well used in traditional patinas as antiquing agents, i.e., darkening certain positive areas of high texture to resemble years of handling, or used to chalk up, attaining a dusty appearance.

Pigmented waxes should never be applied straight from the can to the patinaed surface. First, place the brush in a light wiping motion over the surface of the wax, picking up very little. Then slightly brush it across either a piece of wood or marble to take off any access wax, then apply to the bronze surface. These steps are necessary, as pigmented waxes have the ability to be uncontrollable if applied too heavily. Therefore, always start off with a weak coat and build up as desired.

Many pigmented waxes can be fabricated by

mixing clear wax with many of the same oxides used for patination. Once again, when applying these waxes, start off very sparingly as the pigments used in patination are quite powerful in hue and value, and have the ability to "overdo it" on many bronze patinas. Always experiment with a new combination on a scrap piece of bronze prior to waxing a finished surface.

All of the waxes mentioned above, whether clear or pigmented, may darken a patina when first applied, but as the wax application dries, the patina should reappear. It is always best to apply two thin coats, rather than one heavy layer, as this may dry very unevenly, leaving dark, unwanted patches in the finish. Buffing dried waxes is essential to its protection capabilities in that by rubbing the waxed surface with a soft cloth, it presses and seals the wax, giving a somewhat water resistant finish.

CASEIN

Casein is yet another product used for transferring pigment and metal powders, as well as sealing bronze. Casein is a sticky protein derived from soured milk. It is purchased as a milky liquid that dries clear on bronze, leaving a slight sheen to the surface. Its use goes back many centuries for patination in many European and Asian cultures, where it is used more for transferring color than for sealing.

Casein is applied with a brush, very sparingly, if pigmented, as its transferring ability is great and, once dry, very difficult to remove. Many thin coats may be required in order to attain a specific effect. Pigmented casein is usually applied over Incralac™ and under waxes, as it will tend to bead up on waxed surfaces and inhibit a good seal required for Incralac™.

CHAPTER EIGHT

8

Application Techniques

Patinas are usually applied on the surface of bronze by use of brushes or sprays. There are other application procedures as well, such as dipping, sponging, etc. However, for attaining results given in the following recipes, the author has chosen to describe how chemical compounds are either brushed or sprayed, since these are not only the most traditional, but the easiest applications as well.

The following recipes are considered "hot applications," whereby the bronze surface is heated either by use of torch or oven in order to expand the metal surface, thus allowing reactions from the compounds used to adhere, giving a wide range of color, depth, and even texture for bronze. Hot applications, as a rule, are usually more durable and long lasting than their cold counterparts, making them the most popular worldwide.

Heat is probably the single most important element in the creation of patinas, even more than any one chemical compound used, as heat alone, applied to a bronze surface, has the ability to produce a wide range of coloration.

The trick of using heat for patina application is in its "control." This control can only be mastered by experience. To come to understand what reactions giving color and depth can be achieved from a particular chemical, whether independently or in mixture by means of temperature, makes for a true patineur. This is because the chemical compounds used in the following recipes are given a wide range of color and pattern dependent on various temperatures. A weak solution of ferric nitrate sprayed or brushed on a warm bronze will tend to give a pale yellowish tone; on a surface that is "too" hot, the same mixture may be applied reacting in dark brown, red, and even burgundy hues.

The idea behind heating a bronze prior to chemical application is to distribute surface temperature as evenly as possible. This not only allows for a more even patina, but one of consistent durability as well.

In the following recipes, a propane-driven torch is used and highly recommended, as this gives the patineur better control in achieving and maintaining this even heat required during the patina application. An oven may be substituted for a torch as a heating source in some of the following recipes. However, using an oven greatly reduces many effects that only the open flame of a torch can give. An oven may also overheat many thin and protruding areas of a bronze sculpture, making for an uneven chemical reaction.

As mentioned in Chapter Seven, a handheld propane torch with either a pressure control knob or trigger is recommended. For most bronze sculptures ranging in height from six inches to three feet, a torch tip with a 1½ to 2 inch diameter is most practical. Life-size and monumental bronze castings require much larger torches with four-inch to six-inch tips.

For more information concerning torches, their use and safety, refer to the section on torches in Chapter Seven.

When purchased, many torches will come with instructions for assembly. Follow these instructions in detail to ensure leak-free fits in connections and an unobstructed gas flow. These torches will usually, but not always, require some sort of pressure regulator, usually connected to the propane storage tank. Always follow recommended pressure settings given with individual regulators to ensure that best flame possible, which is a bright blue. Most regulators recommend settings between 30 to 40 P.S.I. The feeder hose that is connected between the pressure regulator and the torch itself must always be untangled and out of traffic areas as well as from under foot. As propane is the most dangerous substance in the art of patination, extreme care must be observed as to its use and storage. Always place the propane tank a safe distance from the ignited torch and never leave a lit torch unattended. Because an open flame is in use, any flammable and/or explosive substance must be kept out of range. Synthetic clothing should never be worn in the area of an open flame as a safety precaution, because this type of clothing can easily melt, adhering to the skin, which usually results in severe burns.

In order to light the handheld torch, first turn the open valve on the top of the propane tank counterclockwise, about a quarter turn. Then check that the regulator reading is set accordingly. If readings are correct, slowly open the control valve on the torch handle, until a hissing is heard coming from the torch tip. (Many trigger types do not have a complete "closed" setting and gas will start being emitted from the tip as soon as the tank is opened.) Using a flint striker, spark at the side of the tip opening until a flame is produced. Many patineurs in other parts of the world usually have a burning candle or oil lamp that is used to ignite their torches as strikers may be hard to come by. In the Americas, strikers have become quite common and should always be used in igniting a propane flame. After the low flame is ignited, then the valve or trigger can be set to attain a wider, hotter blue flame.

As mentioned earlier, heating the bronze surface evenly is of prime importance in achieving an even, durable patina. A metal turntable with either a fire brick or a cinder block on top of the working surface helps in this. The bronze is placed on either one of these surfaces and the heating begins. As a rule, start rotating and heating the bronze from the bottom, usually at the back or side of the piece. Slowly spiral the flame around the piece to the top. Working up and down with the flame will give the bronze an even heat needed. The surface will begin to take on a light amber coloration. This is then the time to apply most patinas. The chemical solution should adhere to the surface, drying instantly when applied by brush or spray. If flashing or oxide washes are required, heat the surface to a medium hot temperature, where the chemical applies, but can be moved before setting by means of reheating. Generally speaking, the hotter the surface, the deeper and tighter the bond. If the bronze begins to develop blue and purple hues on the surface, the bronze is too hot and must be allowed to cool slightly before proceeding.

Always concentrate on undercuts and thicker areas of a casting as these areas usually take more heat in order to reach proper temperatures. These areas also retain their heat longer, whereas thinner areas of a casting will warm up faster and will also cool more rapidly. By truly understanding the casting process, a patineur can come to know what areas of a casting are usually solid and which areas are cast hollow. This information will only help in the application of patinas. If this knowledge is unknown, it will most certainly be discovered while applying compounds. This takes practice as well as patience in understanding and formulating.

Applying chemical compounds from starting at the top of the piece or at the bottom depends on the individual patina, as well as design and mass of the piece. For iridescent copper-base coats, using a ferric nitrate-sodium thiosulfate mixture, always start from the bottom and work up. Many other patinas are applied, however, from the top, as in painting a house, in order to cover spills, runs or spattering down below. As a rule, it is always advisable to apply patinas from the back side and work around to the front.

Also, when using a torch to apply chemicals, unless "flame flashing" or scorching is desired, it is always advisable to wait a few seconds after applying chemicals before resuming with the heating process. When chemicals are first applied to the bronze surface, gasses are being emitted. If the flame from the torch is passed over this area too quickly, these gases will be forced back into the patina, causing a scorching effect in many compounds. However, when a flame is used to flash certain nitrates like silver and ferric nitrate, interesting iridescent patterns of blues, silvers, purples and whites may be produced. This technique may open many exciting paths of color and pattern.

Maintaining an even heat while applying the patina is also of great importance. After the entire piece has been warmed, usually start applying chemicals at the bottom, back side of the piece. The torch should work just ahead of the freshly patinaed area, heating and applying, heating and applying, until the surface is completely covered. With many patina applications requiring such chemicals as cupric nitrate, bismuth nitrate, and zinc nitrate, the patina layer must be rinsed before proceeding. This will help neutralize the chemicals deposited on the surface as well as "set" those particular nitrates into the patina. An added plus to rinsing is that this makes it more difficult to scorch these compounds when reheated.

BASE COAT APPLICATIONS

The key to a successful base coat application is having to start with a clean surface. The surface of bronze is always oxidizing. Some atmospheres tend to speed or slow this process. After a piece is sandblasted, this process begins immediately. It may not be seen for hours or even days. It is therefore always a good idea to apply patinas to bronze as soon as possible after the blasting or sanding process. If a blasted surface is required for a particular patina, continue with chemical applications immediately after blasting. However, for a sanded surface, other steps are recommended for cleaning prior to chemical application.

Machine and hand oils, as well as natural oxidation, have left a sanded surface quite contaminated, thus inhibiting the patina process. Final sanding should be completed, if possible, just prior to patina applications, as this will slow natural contamination. The surface should be wiped clean, using an organic solvent, such as xylol, and left to dry. These solvents also leave unseen, but unwanted chemical deposits that could appear during or after the patina in forms of discoloration. Therefore, it is advisable to rub the bronze surface down using 3M Scotch-Brite™ #96 handpads. Then rub the surface with single "0" or a #1 medium grade steel wool to give a highly-reflective look to a transparent patina.

Pumice can also be used if more of a satin glow is requested. Rottenstone can be used as well, but will tend to shine bronze similar to steel wool and, therefore, is not recommended for a satin look. Rubbing pumice on the surface of the bronze with a soft clean cloth removes most of the remaining contaminate, thus preparing the surface for patinas.

This process of cleaning the surface requires an oil and wax free location with good ventilation to handle organic vapors given off by the cleaning solvents. Always wear rubber gloves during the final cleaning in order to avoid finger prints and smudges. As usual, a proper respirator should always be worn when performing these tasks. Refer to respirators in Chapter Seven.

SULFURATED POTASH (LIVER OF SULFUR)

As a rule, all polysulfides such as liver of sulfur should be applied to a cold bronze surface when used as a base coat. When liver of sulfur is applied to a hot surface, it may become trapped in porous areas, only to leach out later as whitish patches or "pocks" in clusters on the patina, not only disturbing the patina, but bringing attention to an otherwise poor casting. Patinas with a liver of sulfur base coat that have been applied to a hot surface may also tend to darken the overall finished patina at a much faster rate than when applied cold.

When sulfurated potash is sprayed on either a hot or cold surface, certain gases are released into the atmosphere, One such gas that is somewhat toxic in concentrated forms is "hydrogen sulfide." When applied to a hot surface, this gas is liberated in much higher quantities, making for a dangerous breathing environment. Effects from this gas may not be noticed at first, but, with continuous exposure, can cause severe damage to the liver and kidneys. Therefore, if it is decided to apply potassium sulfide to a hot surface, always wear the right protective equipment.

When applying liver of sulfur to a cold surface, use a squirt bottle of the diluted mixture (recipe found in Chapter Seven under sulfurated potash) over the entire piece. It will change from yellow to purple to white and then onto gray. This color change should be gradual. If it changes to gray or black immediately, dilute the mixture more with water before continuing. Start spraying at the bottom and work upward. As the gray coloration develops, concentrate the misting over lighter areas until the entire piece is a dark gray. Rinse with water and continue.

Highlighting liver of sulfur from a cold surface is quite easy using the correct materials. The use of 3M Scotch-Brite™ #96 or #86 handpads has become quite popular for rubbing residues left from the sulfurated potash off of the surface. This leaves shiny, bare bronze on the high points and dark recesses in textured areas. Steel wool can be used as well, either in combination with Scotch-Brite™ handpads, to soften their scratching patterns, or used alone for highlighting, which may tend to leave a darker effect to the base coat, not attaining as much contrast between high and recessed areas of texture as using Scotch-Brite™ handpads. When using both Scotch-Brite™ handpads or steel wool, rinse as you work, to wash away unwanted residues from the liver while also removing steel wool. If left on the surface, steel wool will begin to rust rapidly, causing orange spotting. Once the piece is highlighted to one's satisfaction, it is then ready for heating and for the application of other compound layers.

Using liver of sulfur as an opaque base coat, apply to the surface as mentioned before and rinse. Then heat the bronze slowly and evenly until all signs of moisture have left the surface as well as any porous areas. As the bronze begins to take on a purplish look, remove heat. Using steel wool #1 medium or single "0," rub the entire surface. This will result in a beautiful steel gray base coat that is excellent in accepting all nitrates used except cupric nitrate.

BIRCHWOOD CASEY™ M20

Applying Birchwood Casey™ M20 as an undercoat works much the same as liver. It is sprayed onto a cold surface using a 50-50 mixture of M20 and water until the entire piece turns a blackish brown. Then rinse and heat until all signs of moisture are gone and the bronze begins to take on a slightly bluish color. Using steel wool, rub off the brown residues, exposing a deep bluish-gray base coat, which can be used as a base coat for all of the nitrates mentioned including cupric nitrate.

Ammonium sulfide is applied in the same manner as liver of sulfur, keeping in mind that it is a polysulfide and should be applied to a cold surface for use as a base coat. Highlighting results are similar to that of Birchwood Casey™ M20 or liver of sulfur. The only time that ammonium sulfide is used on a hot surface is in achieving silvery patterns. However, hydrogen sulfide is produced at much higher rates, just as liver of sulfur, when applied to hot metal.

HOT PATINA TECHNIQUES

As mentioned in the beginning of this chapter, the chemical compounds used for the following recipes are applied either by brush or spray. Both applications can give completely different results or those of similarity, all dependent on heat control as well a patina performance. Many patineurs prefer spray methods of attaining many patinas not only because it is usually a quicker process, but many "tight" patterns may be achieved that are not possible when using a brush. The author, although using both techniques, prefers the brush whenever possible as it can be used in a variety of ways that far outnumber the spraying of chemicals. Not only that, far more toxic fumes are emitted with spraying than with brushing. Using brushes to "dab" compounds onto a hot bronze surface usually makes for a stronger patina because the chemicals are actually being pushed into the expanded metal rather than being pulled in from the surface as with sprays. As a traditionalist, the author has learned many brush techniques from patineurs in Asian cultures as well as from excellent patina artists from Europe. Where the brush is functional for both traditional and many contemporary patinas, sprayers are used more on the contemporary side of patination.

The following recipes are applied using both brush and spray, but concentration is given on brush techniques, for reasons mentioned above. As noted earlier, the chemical mixtures should sizzle and adhere to the surface instantly when applied by brush or spray.

BRUSH TECHNIQUES

Brushes come in all shapes and sizes, constructed of a variety of materials. Patina brushes used in the art of patination should always be composed of natural bristles, non-metallic ferrule, and a wooden handle for stirring. Synthetic bristle brushes may be used in waxing a cool surface, or even when buffing a wax finish on a heavily textured surface, but should never be used in patina applications. Synthetic bristles will not only melt when coming in contact with heat, their melting gives off toxic fumes which your respirator may not filter.

Shapes and sizes vary, but the general rule is large brushes for large projects and small brushes for small surfaces. However, when applying most patinas, always use the largest brush possible for the job as this will give a more even coat as well as save time. Never use a brush that is too big for the heated area, as the perimeter of the application may react in scorching when reflamed, and runs in the patina may also result. For the following patinas, brush diameters from one to three inches are recommended. Smaller brushes will be necessary for detail applications seen in many "Multi-patinas."

Brushes come in two shapes, round and flat. Round or "pound" brushes were quite common up until the mid-20th century for painting round shapes, but as flat shapes, especially in architecture, became more popular, new styles and designs were developed and sold much more cheaply, replacing the more expensive round brush. Natural bristle round brushes used for painting may be quite hard to find through hardware and paint supply stores. When they are available, their cost may be too prohibitive for patina applications. Other round brushes that are more acceptable for patina applications than the pound brush is either pastry or glue brushes. These brushes usually have stiff bristles, which is a requirement for many patinas.

Pastry brushes may be purchased from restaurant or bakery suppliers, and glue brushes may be located in art supply stores. For the following recipes, pastry brushes were used, as they usually come with a non-metallic ferrule and are easily accessible.

Round brushes will tend to pull more liquid into the bristle mass than will brushes of flat design. Therefore, never stick the brush deep into the chemical solution. This will overload the brush, making for a disastrous application. Instead, have the brush merely touch the surface of the compound mixture. This usually will pull up more than enough chemical. Experiment and find what is most comfortable. Some patineurs load brushes, shaking out the excess prior to application.

Flat brushes seem to be in every hardware store. However, many of them are made with synthetic bristles, so ensure only natural bristles are purchased for patinas. The cheapest natural bristle brush available is usually the one recommended since a patineur may use many brushes. Some patinas require new brushes to achieve certain effects, while others rely on a well-coated bristle for better transfer. "Chip" brushes are ideal for use in patinas for this reason. They have natural bristles and wooden handles. Their only drawback is their metallic ferrule. However, because of their comparatively low price, they can be disposed of when metal contamination from the ferrule develops.

There should be a separate brush used for each individual compound and mixture. This can add up to quite a few brushes if one wants to reproduce every patina plate given. Using the same brush to apply every chemical will only contaminate solutions, possibly leaving unwanted traces of color in a patina. This is another reason for purchasing inexpensive brushes.

Chemical solutions applied to a bronze surface using a brush should be weaker than those used for spraying. This is because a brush applies more solution to a smaller, more concentrated area. Using high concentrations of chemical mixtures will only build up too quickly, leaving unnecessary texture on the surface as well as unwanted color intensity. Using weak solutions gives the patineur more control and also, through layering, may achieve an illusion of depth that is unattainable with stronger solutions. Strong chemical mixtures are used more for complete solid coats and a brighter effect in coloration. So as a rule, start with a weak solution and strengthen as needed.

Heating the bronze for brush application is much more localized than for spraying. The entire piece should be warmed up, starting from the base area, working upwards. Then return to the bottom and concentrate on heating an area at a time, applying compound mixtures as you go. While applying the patina, heat the area where the application is to continue, until the entire piece is covered. If layering is required, once the first hot application has been applied, start at the top and, gently maintaining heat, work your way back down the surface. If a third layer is required, work from the bottom up once more. This application technique is different for some patinas, but should be followed as a general guideline for patination.

BRUSH PATTERNS

Most patinas are applied with a brush in a dabbing motion rather than in a stroking fashion. This makes for much more control as well as resulting in many exciting effects. Marbleizing is accomplished in the following recipes using a flat chip brush rather than a round brush, because weak solutions are used sparingly. Round brushes may be used as well, but ensure that there is little chemical residue left on the bristles prior to application. Generally, weak chemical solutions are used for marbleizing in attaining depth, brought about by layering. Strong solutions will only block this effect, giving rise to a more solid opaque finish. It is suggested that the patineur study a piece of polished marble first in order to understand its fragmentation, veining, and overall uneven appearance, which gives depth to the stone. When applying chemical compounds to the surface, the flat chip brush can be placed on its side and pulled across the surface to achieve veins, then be dabbed in an uneven fashion to produce fragmentation. Keep heating and applying in a layering fashion until desired effects are achieved.

Dabbing Pattern: Push brush straight onto surface.

Circle or circular patterns are applied in weak solution as well. Bring the bronze up to a medium hot temperature and dab a somewhat loaded brush straight onto the surface, holding it in place for a second or two. Chemicals in the brush will be pulled out onto the surface, depositing the mixture in a ring around the bristles. A chip brush will give an oblong pattern whereas a round brush will tend to leave more of a circular effect. For circular patterns where the center is more opaque, a thicker solution may be required or the addition of certain oxides to the solution will help in achieving opacity.

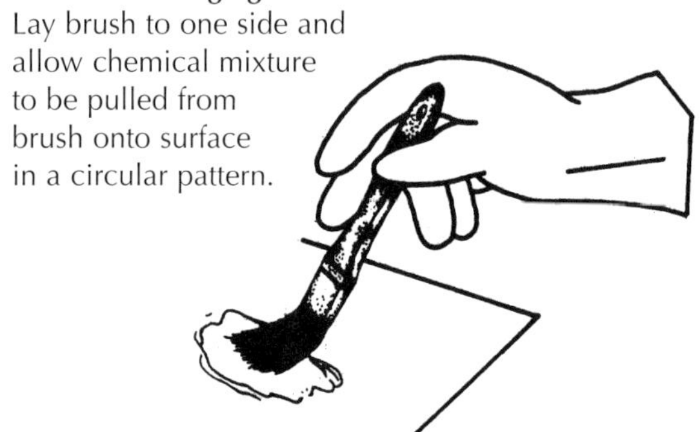

Circular or Ringing Pattern: Lay brush to one side and allow chemical mixture to be pulled from brush onto surface in a circular pattern.

Solid effects require stronger solutions than those used for marbleizing and circular patterns in that opaqueness is the end result. A strong chemical solution is dabbed onto the surface in a layering fashion until one even color is attained. This procedure is used mostly in base coats and multi-patinas, where sharp contrast between one color and another may be required.

Stippling techniques are used when sharp, bright specks or stipples are requested. The lightly loaded brush is applied to a much hotter surface than required for marble or circular patinas and used in a tapping motion, barely touching the surface. This application is usually done quickly and in irregular patterns to achieve sharp contrast between upper and lower base coats.

Stippling Pattern: Barely touch the bronze surface with the brush bristles in a tapping fashion.

Oxide washes involve sandwiching an oxide layer between two translucent nitrate layers. On a hot, clean, sanded surface, dab a ferric nitrate-sodium thiosulfate solution until a rich even copper coloration is attained. Then apply a thin layer of titanium oxide suspended in water over the copper base coat. After this white application is complete, using the same base coat mixture or one that is a tad weaker, wash the oxides merely sitting on the surface down into recessed areas, turning the oxide areas from white to beige. If the ferric nitrate-sodium thiosulfate mixture is too strong, the oxide will be stained more to an orange color rather than a beige. This technique may be layered two to three times, but care should be taken as the ferric nitrate build up will tend to start flaking from the translucent areas of the piece, which is impossible to correct.

Other oxides may be used as well in achieving oxide washes. For example, using chromium oxide, mixed with titanium oxide, will give warmer rich greens to the recessed areas when washed. Oxide black may be mixed with titanium oxide and applied for warm, gray, low-lying areas, etc.

Oxides suspended in water may be used to wash over opaque patinas in order to attain a dusty, soft finish as well. Dipping the brush into titanium oxide/water solution and then dabbing it onto a dry palette containing pigments, prior to application, will enable the patineur to achieve an almost unlimited choice of accent coloration when applied over or sandwiched between nitrate layers.

Oxide washes are not usually recommended for heavily blasted surfaces. Once applied, oxides will tend to be held in the toothing of the blasted surface, unable to wash or move into recessed areas. This effect may cloud a base coat, which may or may not be used to the advantage of the patineur. Experimentation with this is a must.

SPRAY TECHNIQUES

Equipment used for spraying compounds onto a hot bronze surface tend to be a little more sophisticated than basic tools such as brushes. Squirt bottles and airbrushes, either giving a fine spray or spatter pattern, are used. Plastic squirt bottles are excellent in applying patinas because they are corrosion resistant, cheap and readily available. Their spray nozzles may be adjusted to give a fine mist or a steady stream applied across the bronze surface.

Airbrushes are recommended as they will give an even, continuous, fine spray needed for an even patina application. Air brushes tend to be somewhat costly, especially where patinas are concerned, in that stainless steel models containing stainless or glass reservoirs are usually recommended as they inhibit chemical corrosion. Fluid assemblies or nozzle tips may become clogged easily when using certain compounds and, therefore, should be cleaned on a regular basis. Many solutions containing oxides will clog a fine airbrush.

Air brushes are sold in a variety of designs and sizes. Larger "paint sprayers," such as those used for painting car bodies, may be used in patina applications on large monumental surfaces. Small pencil point airbrushes are preferred for smaller detail work.

The use of an airbrush always requires the incorporation of compressed air. Small air compressors are available for the hobbyist, but for the professional patineur, a larger compressor will be needed, not only for an airbrush, but for sanding and blasting the surface as well. When using compressed air through an airbrush, it is a good idea to use some form of air drying equipment to extract any traces of water and oil from the compressed air prior to use. Either of these contaminates in compressed air may end up on the bronze surface, spotting or staining the applied patina. This may not show up immediately, but if the water and oil are there, eventually they will appear. Water and oil are detrimental to the air assembly parts of the airbrush as well, causing irregular air flow and trigger malfunction. Also, clean compressed air is recommended for lacquer and varnish applications because, once again, oil and water can be sprayed onto the surface, spotting and staining, not to mention interfering with a complete seal.

Heating the surface of the bronze takes a little more concentration for spray techniques than those for brush work. This is, of course, only if an even patina is required. Heating the bronze for spray techniques is similar to that required for brushing, in that heating begins at the bottom, preferably at the back or side of the piece, and the torch flame is gradually moved upward in spiraling fashion. However, for spraying an even coat of patina mixture over the surface, instead of returning back to the bottom and concentrating on an area as for brush patinas, the torch is moved across all areas of the piece in sweeping motions, heating not only the surface, but the surrounding air as well, duplicating the environment of an oven. Once the surface begins to take on an even amber hue, spraying commences. Also, as in brush techniques, wait a few seconds before returning the flame to the patinaed surface, allowing gases emitted from the hot application to dissipate, thus avoiding scorches and flashing.

As noted earlier, compound mixtures for spraying are usually more concentrated than those solutions used in brush applications. Spraying a compound mixture can cover more surface at a quicker rate than brush applications. To obtain color range intensities with brush patinas, a stronger mixture is necessary as well. This does not mean that weak solutions should not be sprayed. The author recommends spraying weak solutions, not as weak as for brush applications, but not much stronger either. This may make for thin applications, giving transparency and depth to many patina overlays.

Solid effects are best accomplished with an airbrush, as squirt bottles tend to spot, causing an irregularity in an otherwise opaque even coat. This is not to say that squirt bottles should not be used for solid even coats. If the misting is fine enough and the sweeping movement of the patineur is even, then the patina will be even also. However, an airbrush is so much easier and quicker, which makes it preferred by most professional patineurs.

It is best to begin layering the compounds over the surface in various directions as to fill any thin lines between spray paths. Translucent effects are the most popular spraying techniques used, whereby one is able to see the metal below or through the patina. The best known of this type of patina is what is called "French brown," achieved by using ferric nitrate misted over a highlighted liver of sulfur base coat. An almost endless variety of color hue and value may be obtained in this basic patina—everything from light yellow to dark translucent burgundy. This is also one of the easiest transparent patinas to achieve as ferric nitrate is the only true transparent nitrate used in patinas.

Any other nitrates used for transparency are usually sprayed on in thin coats and then, when lacquered or waxed hot, they will tend to take on the appearance of translucency, trapping a light film of color between the shinny bronze and the sealer.

Marbleizing effects are quite popular in the art of patination. However, using a sprayer for creating the look of marble may be more difficult than with a brush, but once accomplished, can give far more interesting results. By adjusting the squirt bottle spray tip to provide a steady stream, it can be used for creating veins and fragmentation. Layering with fine mists, alternating back and forth between these two, will add depth and dimension. A few spatters here and there should also be incorporated for added interest.

Flame flashing may actually be categorized under marbleizing in that similar patterns may appear, only in brighter flashier colors, i.e., iridescent purples, bright silvery patterns, white and blue multi-patterns, etc. Compound solutions to be flashed are first sprayed on a medium hot surface, and then the torch is immediately drawn across the patina applied, pushing emitted gasses back into the patina, thus "setting" many newly formed compounds in irregular patterns. Patinas created by means of flashing tend to be somewhat uneven, and so flashing is recommended for smaller bronzes. It will take time and practice to gain control of this technique, but the results can be worth it. Chemicals that are heat sensitive, making them excellent for flashing, are ferric nitrate, silver nitrate, cupric nitrate and zinc nitrate.

Granite effects are accomplished using squirt bottles set to spatter or incorporating the use of a spatter gun. The patterns of granite are much more uniform than those of marble, so achieving an even spatter pattern is important. The easiest way of obtaining this even application of spatter is to use a spatter gun, which is no more than a worn out airbrush that no longer gives a fine mist but spits chemical solutions. The fluid assembly tip may be widened with a drill or nail in order to allow a spatter action to occur. Another way to achieve spattering is to shoot chemical solutions through an airbrush that is designed to transfer thick liquids, such as paint, etc. By transferring patina mixtures (with the consistency of water) through these, the airbrush will tend to spatter, or speck, the compounds onto the bronze surface. These airbrushes can give such excellent results that even master stone carvers have a hard time telling some patinas from actual stone.

Granite patinas are usually applied by layering two or more chemical mixtures, alternating coats, until the desired effect is obtained. This granite technique has a wide range from translucent to completely opaque characteristics.

Weak chemical solutions are recommended for most granite patinas as strong concentrates may be too bright and overpowering as under or overlays. Also, concentrated solutions may tend to leave patina texture developed by means of spattering. It is not recommended to rinse granite patinas after application as this will cause patterns to shift, enabling oxides to wash, disrupting flow in the patina pattern.

MULTI-PATINAS

A style of patination that became vogue during the decline of the Victorian era was that of multi-patinas, or many different patinas on one sculpture. This brought more attention to detail, bringing a piece of figurative sculpture that much closer to realism. Traditionally, colors used for this style are kept somewhat subdued, keeping the entire piece of art compatible and moving. When chemical mixtures are used that are too intense in coloration, the flow of the entire piece may be broken. Color compatibility is another problem to contend with when choosing multi-patina techniques, as this may also "break up" the composition of a piece. Remember, when selecting colors, keep in mind that this is bronze, and not ceramic figurines. Choosing the right patinas can give a bronze a rich, eye-catching appeal, making the sculpture pleasing to the eye. Traditional patinas applied using multi-patina techniques tend to use more subdued rich tones, as opposed to using brighter colors to induce humor on a more contemporary piece. Working with multi-patinas has the ability to "ground" a piece or make it "float." Choosing lighter coloration toward the top of the piece, and gradually working in darker tones toward the base, will tend to ground the piece. Just the opposite effect may tend to float the object. Lighter colors will usually suspend sculpture, where dark colors may tend to give it mass.

SELECTIVE HIGHLIGHTING

When releasing or removing a liver of sulfur base coat, instead of rubbing the entire surface, rub back selected areas that are chosen to be lighter, such as skin surfaces, certain articles of clothing, etc. (These areas may also be "spot blasted" to make for an even lighter surface.) Leaving other areas darker or even black will already begin the basics of a simple multi-patina. In many cases, this may be all that is necessary, along with various concentrations of ferric nitrate, to achieve a very tasteful patina. Highlighting specific areas after the patina application is complete adds even more dimension. These surfaces of extreme highlight may be rubbed with brass, or silver polish, or a paste of baking soda and lemon juice, to bring up polished edges, small articles of clothing, etc., in order to give a "glitz" to the final result.

Heating a bronze for multi-patinas is achieved and maintained in select areas. Always heat and apply darker colors first, working up to lighter tones. Blue or white are usually the last colors to be applied as any over spray or spatter will affect their coloration.

FOIL TECHNIQUES

Foil techniques such as gold and silver leaf applications are the last steps prior to sealing a multi-patina. The bronze surface should be at room temperature or cooler in order to apply gluing agents such as quick drying varnishes. Warm surfaces will force them to set up and dry too quickly, and areas that are too cold will not allow these varnishes to set up at all. This type of varnish comes as a fast drying form that sets up in 20 minutes or so, or as a varnish of slower drying time allowing leaf application to begin in 12 hours. The fast drying varnish has a small disadvantage in that large areas cannot be covered in the short application time this varnish allows. Therefore, the slower setting varnish is recommended for larger surfaces, as this allows much more "tactable" time in which to apply leaf. These quick drying varnishes are painted on the surface, very sparingly and neatly, using a soft sable varnish or paint brush, or a soft sponge. The fast drying varnish will begin to set up in 20 minutes or so. The best way to tell when these varnishes are ready to accept leaf is to tap the surface with a knuckle. If it sticks, wait a few minutes and tap again. If it "pops," it is ready. Using either a "gilder's brush" or a soft sable brush, gently rub your hair with the bristles, building up static electricity, then touch the leaf to be applied. The static electricity will pull the foil up and hold it to the bristles, until it touches the varnished surface. Applying many pieces, overlaying as quickly as possible is the key. Allow it to sit a few minutes and, gently using a clean sable brush, in a sweeping motion, push down to seal the leaf and remove any excess. The tiny pieces of excess foil may become lodged in deep texture on lower parts of a multi-patina; therefore, masking with aluminum foil is suggested to inhibit this. If working on a larger surface where more than just accent areas of gilding are required, always start from the bottom and work up, both in varnish and leaf application.

The finished gilded surface should be left to dry for another 12 to 24 hours (longer for slow drying varnishes) before applying a spray sealer. The gold or silver areas may then be antiqued or enriched using pigmented casein or waxes.

Recommended base coats for gold are black, red, or green. Since gold and silver leaf are somewhat translucent, these various undercoats affect the "tones" of the metal leaf; i.e., black used under gold will give more of a pale gold color; red will make the gold rich, adding an orange warmth; and green will tend to yellow or make what is called "lemon" gold. Black is always recommended for silver as this makes for a dark, deep, rich effect.

This type of foil application results in more of an antique, soft look rather than a bright, burnished one. Special gessoes are required for bright burnishes, which are much harder to achieve and rarely used in combination with patinas. The undercoats may be patinas, but fast drying lacquers or enamels are traditionally used, as these will give a smoother, glossier look to the adhered foil. Patinaed surfaces may leave a dull, non-glossy finish which may be more in line with subtle coloration changes. Gently using very fine steel wool on the dried foil surface will bring up the undercoat, resulting in an even more antique appearance.

MASKING TECHNIQUES

When applying more than one patina to a piece or when requesting a sharp change in color, masking certain areas may be required to avoid over spray, resulting in unwanted "halo" effects of coloration. Thin cardboard may be used to shield or mask a certain area. If an oven is used for heating, masking tape may be used. Never use masking tape with torch heat as it will burn and stick to the surface, resulting in a real mess.

One of the best masking mediums to be used in the art of patination is a heavy duty aluminum foil. It can be crimped to conform to a sculpted surface, and it holds its shape under an open flame. Not only is it great as an overspray guard, it also can be used to keep certain areas cooler or from becoming scorched or flashed.

There are many industrial masking agents on the market today, many of them sensitive to heat. Only choose these masking products that will not burn under 500°F. These agents come in liquid form and are painted onto the surface, usually in two or three coats. Once dry, they become elastic, which makes for an excellent masking tool.

ANTIQUING METHODS

There is almost an unlimited choice of techniques used to make a traditional patina appear antique. Basic applications are carried out using pigmented waxes, brushed over certain areas to give a rich appearance similar to that caused by hand oils. Rottenstone may be lightly placed on a rag and rubbed gently over the sealed patina to give more of a dusty appearance. Mixed with casein, rottenstone may be layered along with many pigments to obtain a thin glaze of color over a sealed patina.

Clean wax mixed with carbon and/or oxide black and then applied to the recessed areas of a surface is the most common antiquing method, as this will give a darker overall appearance to a finished bronze. (This mixture is also great for hiding unwanted investment deposits discovered in a finished patina.)

Gently rubbing selected areas of a finished patina with pumice to remove layers may add to an antique finish as well. Steel wool may also be substituted in attaining this effect, but it tends to leave the area shiny, rather than dull as with pumice.

There are many other combinations in which to antique a piece of art work, such as using vinegar to streak, ammonia to give a bluish dusty effect, etc. An entire volume could be written on just antique methods, but hopefully this will give the patineur an idea of what can be accomplished. Countries such as Thailand, India, Nepal, China, Japan, and Indonesia specialize in antique appearances, enough to fool experts of antiquity in many museums around the world.

ACRYLIC APPLICATIONS

Acrylic artists' paints may be used to obtain coloration not attainable by the use of compound mixtures. The acrylic paints create a better bond, in many cases, to the bronze surface than do nitrates. They will usually hold coloration better over extended periods of time than many chemical patinas. However, it is always recommended to use acrylics in combination with patina layers to soften and blend their otherwise powerful color intensity.

Acrylic paints should always be watered down to the consistency of chemical compounds and applied basically the same way, only using less heat. Spattering or spraying are usually not recommended unless used in a real weak solution because they will tend to leave a texture, due to the acrylic binders. Therefore, because acrylics can have powerful color intensity, in a wide assortment of hues, it is best to choose those colors that will be tasteful when used in combination with chemical patinas. Never depend solely on acrylics for color as this may run the risk of a "tacky" finish, not at all resembling the warmth and richness of a bronze patina.

CHAPTER NINE

Choosing The Right Patina

Probably one of the most difficult decisions that faces the sculptor who is casting in bronze is choosing the right patina. There are many variables or guidelines that may help in deciding which patina is best suited for a particular sculpture. Working with a master patineur may be of tremendous help, for not only will this patina artist be more familiar with surfaces similar to the one in question, he or she will also know what may bring a particular surface to the forefront or subdue its form. A master patineur may also pick up certain coloration ideas from emotions expressed by the sculptor during conversations regarding the sculptor's work that is in question.

Always, when choosing coloration for bronze sculpture, remember that it is first and far most, bronze. In most cases there has been a considerable amount of time, energy and money spent on producing a work of art in this medium, and it would be a shame to ignore this for the sake of choosing a wrong patina. For example, the sculptor has produced a swan in flight. The sculptor is limiting himself or herself by looking at this object as a swan in flight, instead of seeing it as it really is, i.e., a bronze of a swan in flight. Choosing coloration that will not only bring out the medium of bronze, but also give life, character, and individualism to this particular swan is paramount.

Design and style play major roles in deciding on just the right patina. If the design and style are more traditional, then it might be suggested to look at traditional patinas rather than those of contemporary style, because many contemporary patinas may disturb subtle flow and movement in a more traditional piece. The same idea goes for contemporary bronzes, where traditional patinas may inhibit the true art form from becoming fully expressed.

Certain styles of representational work, whether it be realistic or abstract, have a wider range of patina choices than do others. Many of these choices may be based on emotion; a realistic figurative bust commissioned as a memorial would never use bright multi-patinaed effects as this might detract from a somber or stately pose. Using multi-patinas on memorial busts in general are considered in bad taste, and therefore, should be avoided. Multi-patinas, especially when using bright, rich colors, are more suited for themes of humor and/or for drawing attention to detail. It is always a good idea to keep in mind the flow and movement of a piece when deciding on specific colors to be used tastefully in a multi-patina. Too many bright colors may fight color compatibility, causing the eye to jump around the surface from one color to the next, breaking up the piece, rather than creating a possible flow that may be achieved by balancing bright colors with softer, deeper tones.

When choosing patinas, whether single or multi, the surface itself plays one of the most important roles. Many patinas have been developed for use on textured or modeled surfaces in order to make such surfaces read well. These patinas tend to be boring or without life on a smooth, untextured surface. Many patinas that require a smooth surface may break up flow in a textured area. Certain patterns that give a particular patina its uniqueness may be lost all together in heavily textured surfaces. The following plates give the reader an idea of how individual patinas will work on smooth and textured surfaces. Some of these patinas will accentuate texture while others will cover it up all together. Still other patinas will blend texture, making for a softer surface.

The surface finish is the foundation of the applied patina, and so this is yet another consideration in the choice of patinas. Usually, considerable work goes into the creation of a smooth surface, requiring hours of sanding, both mechanically and manually. It seems such a waste of time and money simply to blast or cover up this work, especially when there are so many patinas that will work well in reflecting such labor, not to mention bringing more depth and richness to a patina finish.

Another consideration in deciding on the right patina is its location, i.e., indoors or out, good lighting or poor, etc. The choice of patinas for bronzes being placed indoors far outnumber those destined for outdoor exposure. Patinas on indoor bronzes tend to be lighter than those for outdoors, simply because they allow the bronze surface to read better under artificial light, whereas darker patinas may hide movement as well as detail. Of course, there are always exceptions to this rule.

Patinas chosen for bronze surfaces that are to be exposed to the elements must be quite durable unless change is anticipated. Certain compounds used in the following patina recipes react differently under sunlight, changing color by means of producing new compounds within the patina. Others react to moisture exposure more rapidly, becoming chalky and lighter, eventually taking on light turquoise traces of copper hydroxide. Some patinas may be too delicate for outdoor use, as their unique patterns may distort or disappear completely from the surface.

Taking into account the bronzes' immediate surroundings is also of prime importance when looking at patinas. This has much more to do with outdoor placement than indoor placement. Certain patterns of color found in the immediate surroundings of a sculpture may be reflected off of its patinaed surface, interfering with flow and form. Hot colors of yellow or red in some patinas may be cooled somewhat by the surrounding of a green landscape. Light patinas may be more suited against a dark background, and darker patinas against lighter ones, as in buildings, walls, etc. If a bronze is to be placed in an area shaded by trees, solid patinas are preferred over those with patterns, as patterns within many patinas will tend to camouflage sculpture. All patinas are of interest in full sunlight, but patinas of richness, with depth and/or pattern, tend to draw more attention than those of simpler composition.

Much of the bronze work that is to be placed outdoors is exposed to the public. Based on opinion, more conservative values of color might be recommended, as bright, unfamiliar tones may mislead the viewer as to the medium chosen, not to mention that bright colors in 3D can be somewhat overpowering. Usually, the idea of choosing a patina for a bronze sculpture to be placed outdoors is to tie into or work with its surroundings, as opposed to being set sharply apart or fighting against it. A simple green or brown patina may work much better positioned in the midst of a flower bed than one of hot, reflective colors or busy patterns. These tend to work better against large planes of cool color, as in a lawn, the sky, or even against a white wall.

When choosing a patina, it is best to have as few decision obstacles as possible. For example, it is never recommended to choose a patina for an individual casting based solely on the attached base type and color. Many new sculptors will tend to choose stone or wood bases because of their unique striations, unusual color combination, etc. These bases, especially in stone, might be more suited for a geological exhibit than used for basing bronze, as they may tend to draw attention away from the sculpture. Simple dark bases will tend to "ground" a piece, while white or light colored bases may allow a bronze to float. When in doubt, always choose black marble or granite as everything goes elegantly with black.

It is always helpful for the sculptor to have photographs of desired patinas on hand when discussing coloration choices with a patineur. Please keep in mind, however, that very few photographers and darkroom personnel reproduce true color. Photographers, like patineurs, are to enhance the style and forms of the piece. Certain artificially colored lights are used to evoke emotion with a piece. Although this art of lighting in photography is used to show an exquisite product, this same lighting may also give false coloration to the patina, making it impossible to reproduce chemically. If in doubt, the master patineur can usually tell. Reproducing these photographs for magazines, etc., may bring a variety of different colors as well, which may also be impossible to reproduce. When choosing photos for patina decisions, try to choose those showing surfaces of similarity to the bronze in question. Showing pictures of brightly-patterned patinas on smooth surfaces will only be frustrating when dealing with a heavily-textured bronze.

CHAPTER TEN

10

The Recipes

All of the patina recipes listed have been used time and time again with great results. These particular recipes were chosen for this book as they give the reader a good idea of color and pattern range that may be achieved by the use of only the most basic chemical compounds used in the art of patination. These patinas are also some of the easiest to reproduce, although because there are so many variables that allow patina variations, both during and after each application, the following recipes should be used more as basic guidelines. Each patineur has developed his or her particular style, just as the sculptor, and this is usually seen as a result of unique individual application techniques. No two patineurs will obtain exactly the same results, giving this art an almost unlimited perspective.

It was decided that measurements used in the following recipes be calculated in teaspoons, tablespoons, and liquid ounces, as opposed to grams and liters. Although this practice of measurement is taboo in the science of chemistry, patination is very much an art, and in most cases, a milliliter or milligram is not going to make much of a difference. Also, these types of measurements were chosen as they are most common and inexpensive. Besides, most art students and small foundries may find purchasing a triple beam scale, or other such weighing devices, too expensive for occasional use. Many larger foundries and independent patineurs have purchased great scales, only to have them sit on a shelf, weighing the dust that accumulates on their tables. All measuring spoons should be composed of plastic, not metal, and measuring cups should be composed of glass or plastic. Plastic or glass containers (such as those used for storing food, etc.) are recommended for use in preparing the following chemical mixtures. Never use metal containers such as empty coffee cans, as metal contamination from these cans or other metal utensils may be developed. Also, as a common sense safety measure, never use containers that would later be used for food. Plastic or glass containers in the shape of bowls are perfect for mixing solutions and, if they have lids, this is an added bonus as many of these mixtures can be stored and used at a later date.

Most patineurs tend to eye their measurements of chemical mixtures, as this is what is most comfortable to them. For a novice or apprentice, however, it is recommended to follow the suggested measurements in the following recipes to become acquainted with the various strengths and colors or patterns they create. As one becomes more familiar with these chemicals and their unique characteristics, mechanical measurement may no longer be necessary. (There are patinas that do require exact measurements, but none of those are listed in this book.)

If certain chemical mixtures are not working out on the surface as anticipated, a few more crystals of the binding nitrate or an extra pinch of oxide may be in order, adding yet another unique aspect to a patineur's palette.

The following patinas should never be used on surfaces that may come into contact with foods. Many of the chemical compounds used in patinas are quite poisonous and may transfer into food, poisoning the one who eats it. This goes for fruit that must be peeled as well.

The recipes listed all follow the same format. This is for easy comparison and evaluation. The ***style***, whether traditional, contemporary, or in a few cases classical, gives the reader the category of patina recommended. The ***technique*** explains the basic application used to obtain a certain style. The ***effect*** describes the color and pattern of the finished patina. ***Chemical mixtures*** are listed in accordance with their applications. Measurements for the chemical mixtures used are listed at the beginning of the recipes. ***Surface preparation*** is the recommended finish that works best for a particular patina. Whether the surface is blasted or sanded, it must always be clear of oils (both machine and hand), grease, or any other foreign substance that will interfere with the patina. The ***application*** part of the recipe takes the patineur through the process, step by step, from beginning to end. There are usually variations to every patina. Some patinas have too many ***variations*** to mention them all. Therefore, they have been compiled whenever possible. ***Remarks*** are usually made concerning the stability, durability, and overall performance of a particular patina. This reference will come in handy when choosing the right patina.

MIXING COMPOUNDS

When mixing the following compounds, it is always advisable to start with a weak solution and test the concentration on scrap bronze before proceeding. Strengthen the mixture as desired, but do not over-concentrate, as strong solutions tend to build up and flake off the surface. Those thick deposits that remain can add unwanted texture to the bronze surface and make the process of neutralizing incomplete.

Experiment with mixing the following compounds, but always read the incompatible properties associated with each compound found in their Material Safety Data Sheets prior to mixing. New chemical compounds added to the patina palette can expand the range of coloration while adding an entirely new line of effects.

The novice and apprentice must experiment with each compound in order to better understand its unique properties. By understanding these properties the patineur can become more efficient in their applications as well as come to know and understand their final results. Even the master patineur learns something from each patina applied.

Patina Plates

LIST OF PATINAS

#101 Antique Black
#102 Transparent Antique Gold
#103 Antique Gray
#104 Old World Green
#105 Opaque Brown
#106 Grecian Blue
#107 Mottled Turquoise
#108 French Brown
#109 Chinese Brown
#110 Classic Brown
#111 Tortoise Shell
#112 Traditional Ochre
#113 Butterscotch
#114 Antique Burgundy
#115 Italian Gold
#116 Cherokee Red
#117 Transparent Gold
#118 Apple Green
#119 Verde Brown
#120 Brownish Gray
#121 Iridescent Red Brown
#122 Blue Speckle
#123 Moroccan Blue
#124 Dusty Copper Oxide Wash
#125 Green Oxide Wash
#126 Atlantic Blue
#127 Salmon
#128 Transparent Green and Red
#129 African Soap Stone
#130 Contemporary Ochre
#131 Fuchsia Pink
#132 White (Marble White)
#133 Contemporary Ochre Oxide Wash
#134 Arctic Soap Stone
#135 Lapis Lazuli
#136 Opaque Yellow
#137 Idaho Granite
#138 Multi-Layered Oxide Wash
#139 Amber Marble
#140 Silver
#141 Gold Flash
#142 Dutch Blue
#143 Rusty Blue Marble
#144 Autumn Marble
#145 Black Marble
#146 Green Marble
#147 Gilt Brown
#148 Camouflage
#149 Dakota White Marble
#150 Pink Marble
#151 Gray Onyx
#152 Spanish Moss
#153 Roman Brown
#154 Red Marble
#155 Blue Wave
#156 Brown Marble
#157 Mars Red
#158 Aqua Marine
#159 Italian Marble
#160 Brown Lace
#161 Persian Brown Marble
#162 Gray Marble
#163 Blue Nymph
#164 Gray Granite
#165 Transparent Brown Granite
#166 Green Granite
#167 Red Granite
#168 Rocky Mountain Granite
#169 Blue Granite
#170 Silver Granite
#171 Ancient Green
#172 Chiang Green

Antique Black #101

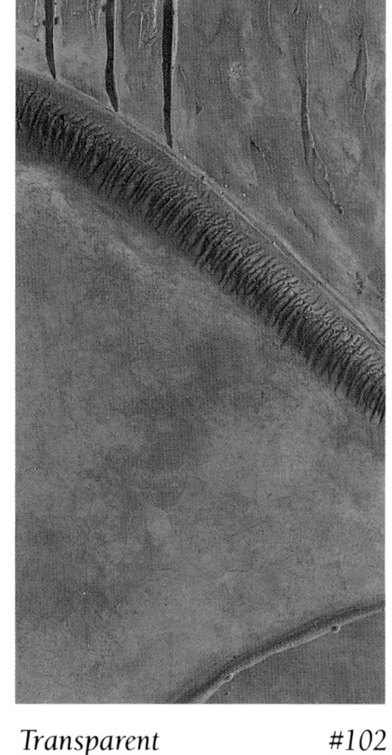

Transparent Antique Gold #102

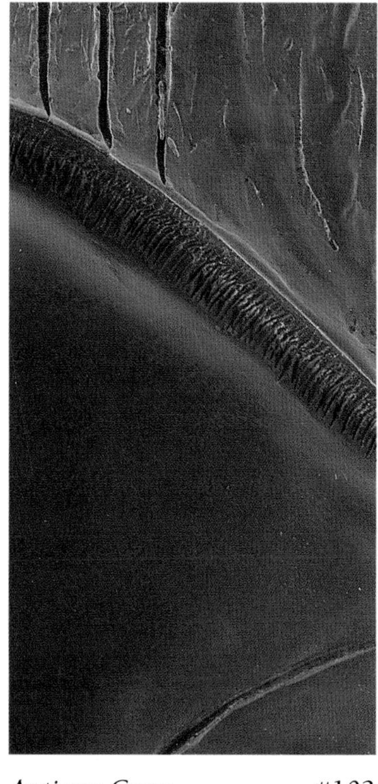

Antique Gray #103

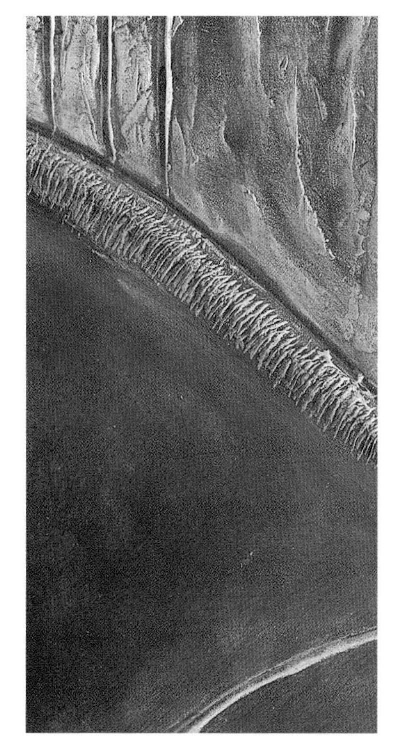

Old World Green #104

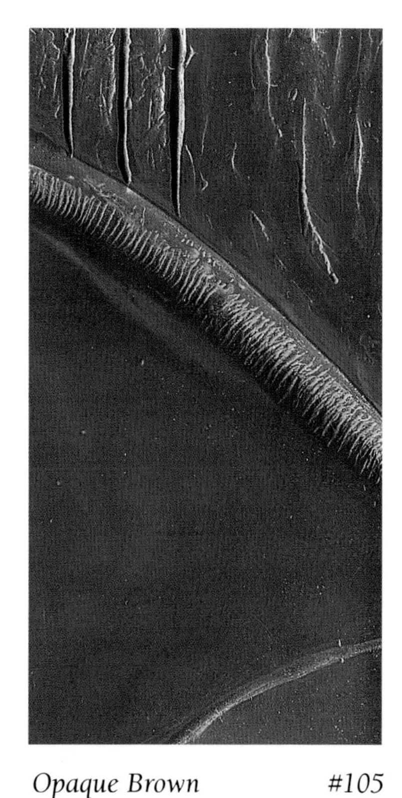

Opaque Brown #105

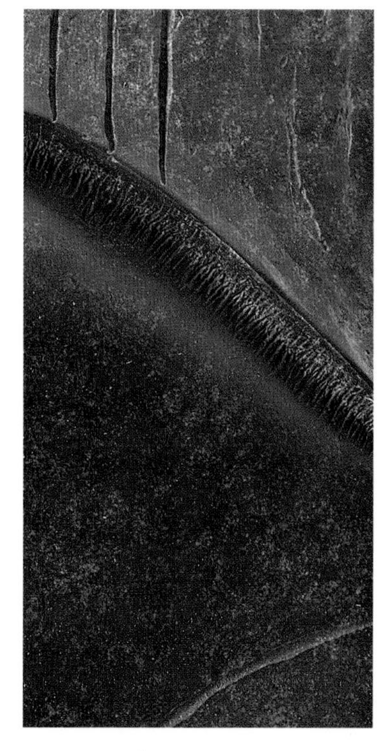

Grecian Blue #106

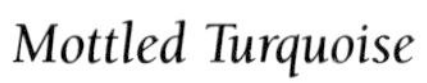

Mottled Turquoise #107

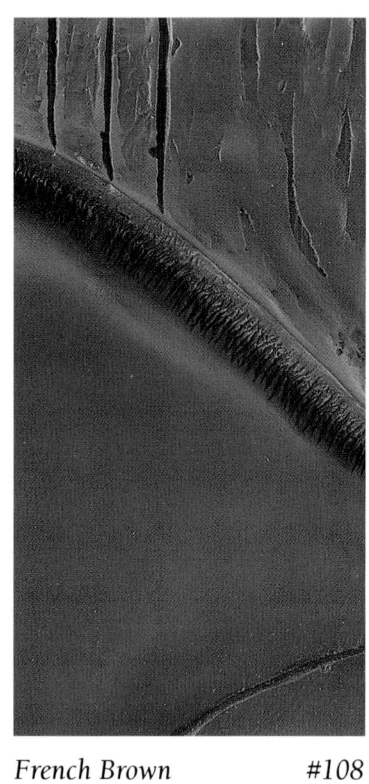

French Brown #108

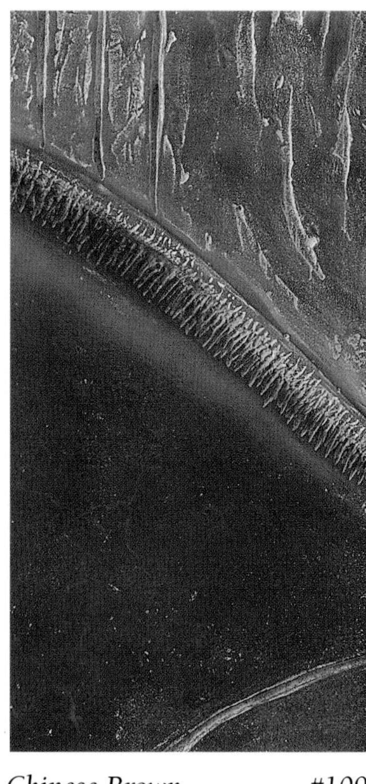

Chinese Brown #109

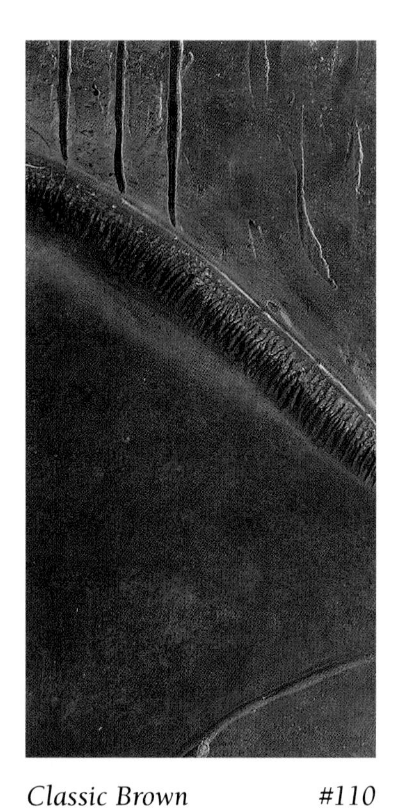

Classic Brown #110

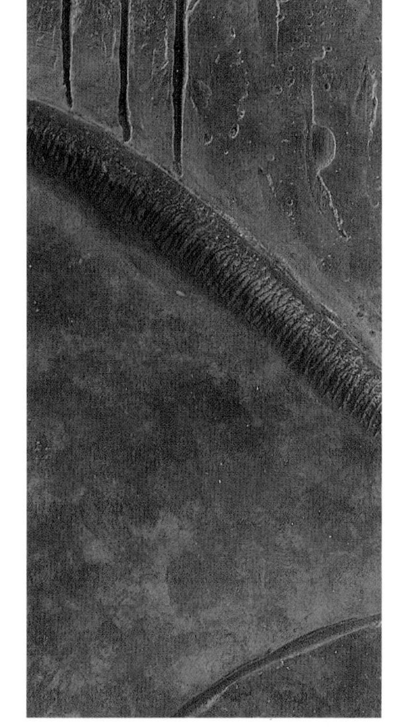

Tortoise Shell #111

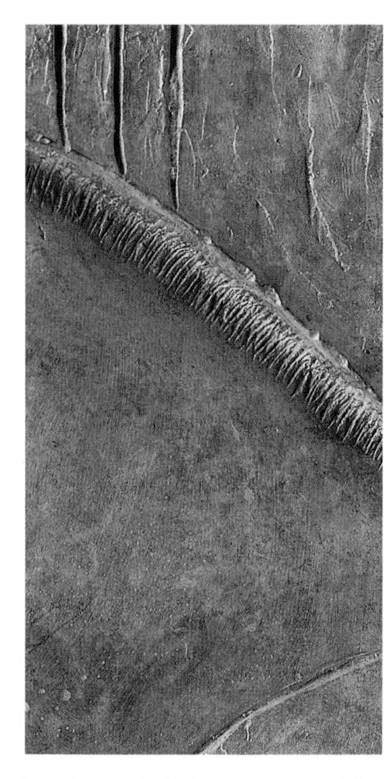

Traditional Ochre #112

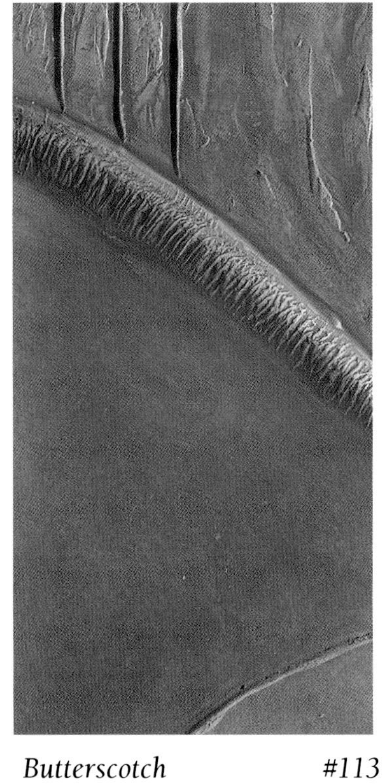

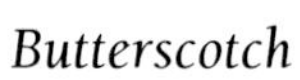

Butterscotch #113

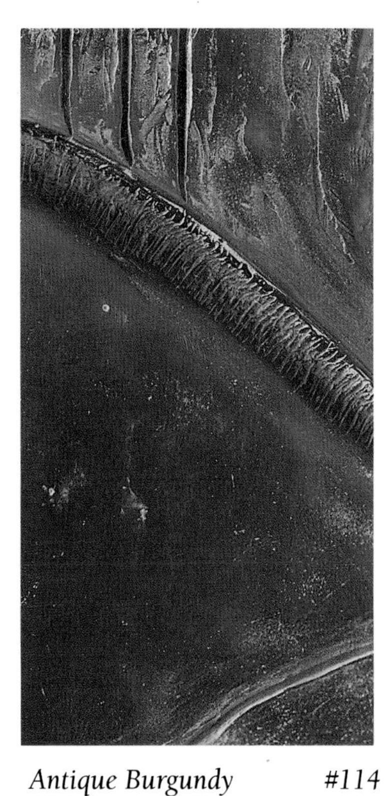

Antique Burgundy #114

Italian Gold #115

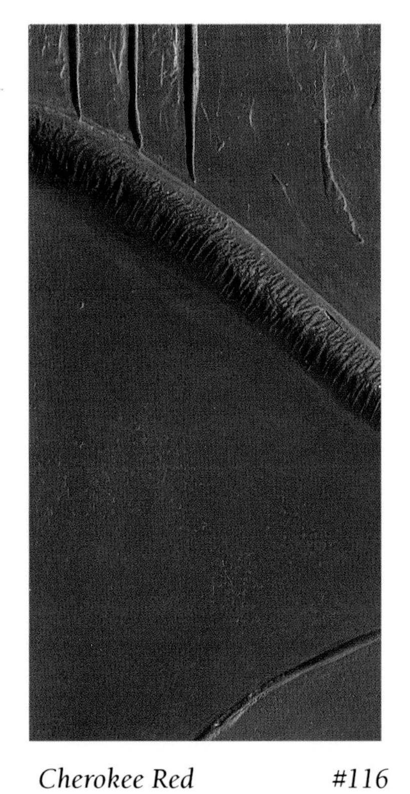

Cherokee Red #116

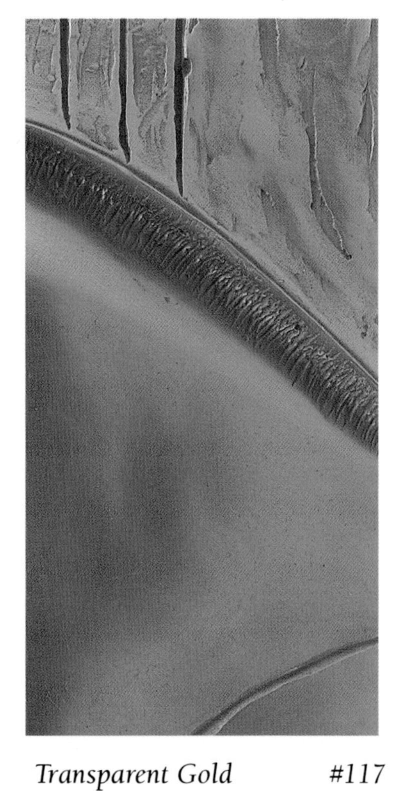

Transparent Gold #117

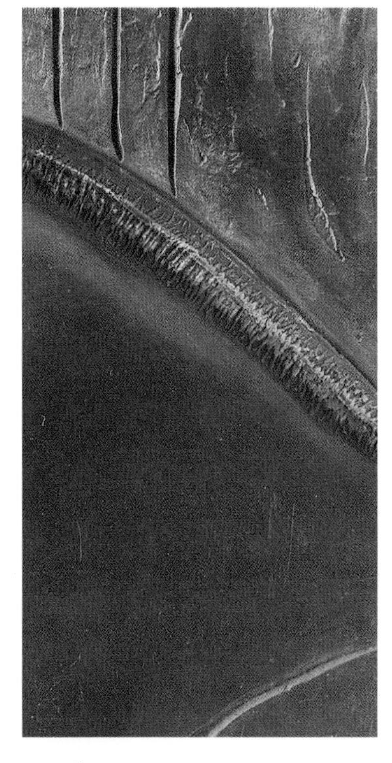

Apple Green #118

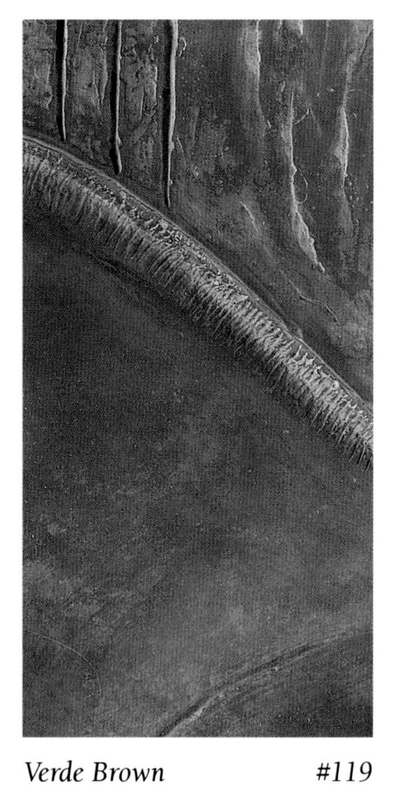

Verde Brown #119

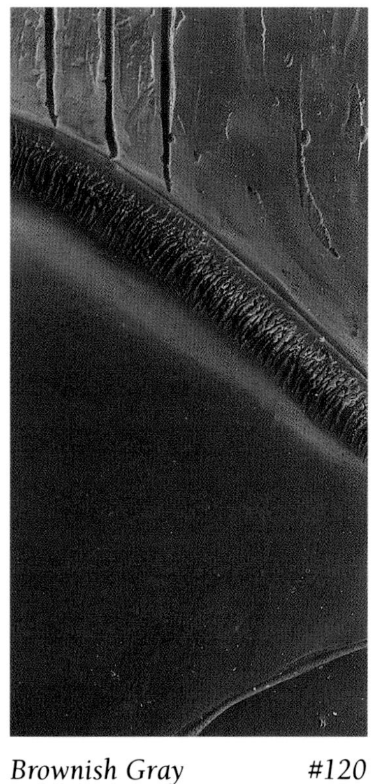

Brownish Gray #120

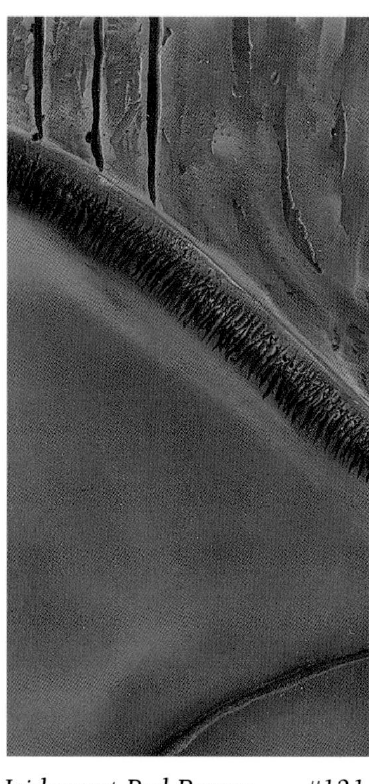

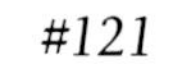

Iridescent Red Brown #121

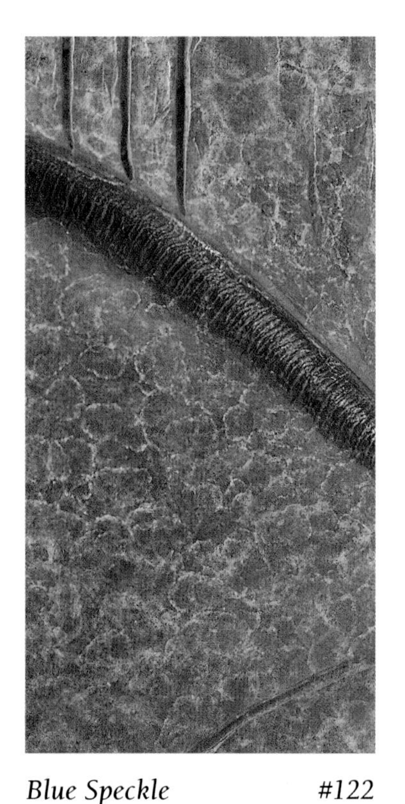

Blue Speckle #122

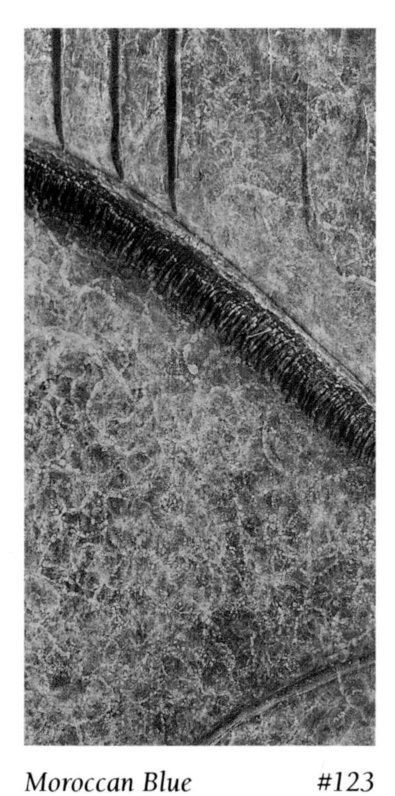

Moroccan Blue #123

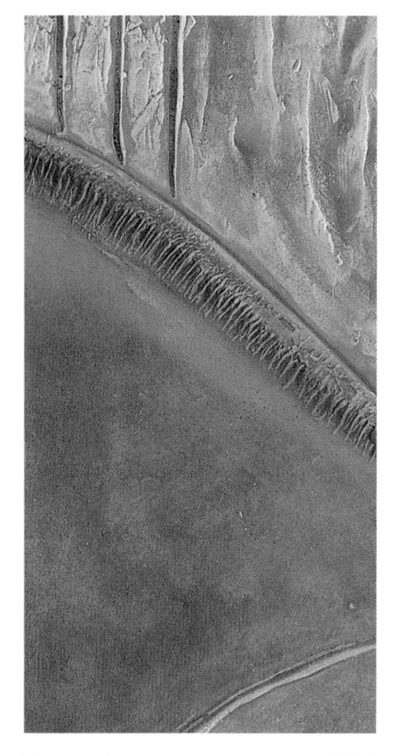

Dusty Copper Oxide Wash #124

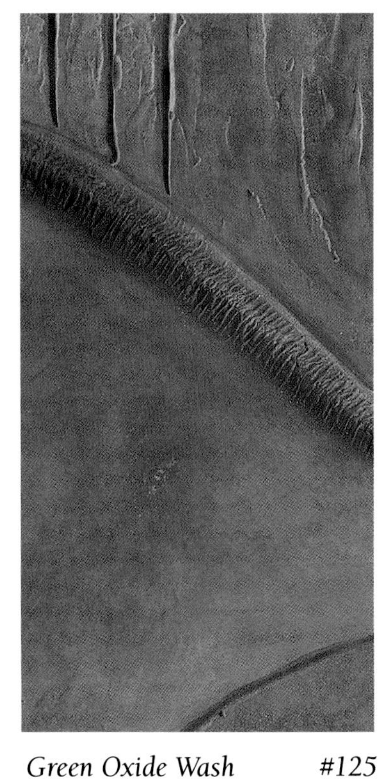

Green Oxide Wash #125

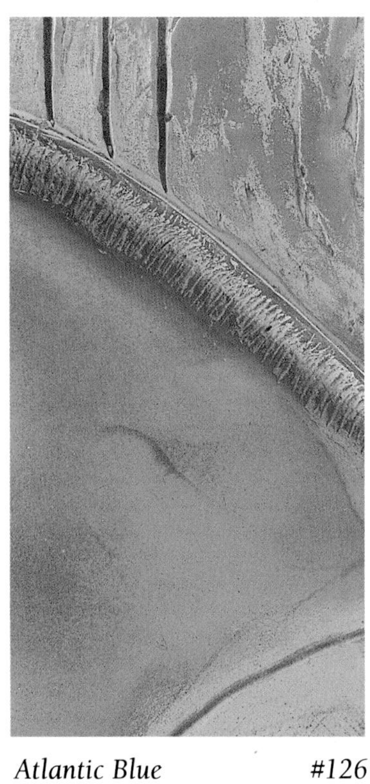

Atlantic Blue #126

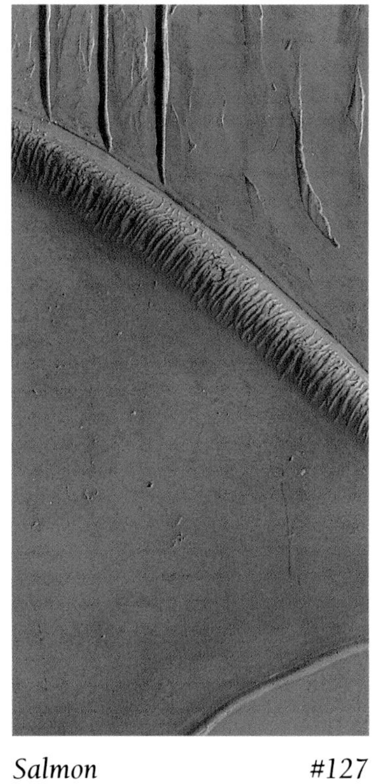

Salmon #127

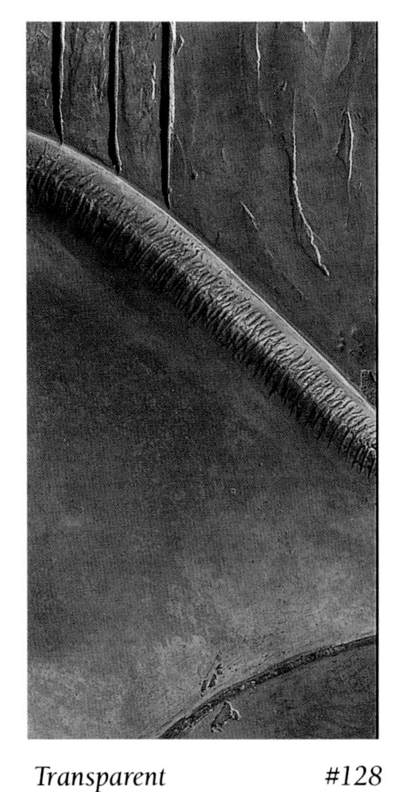

Transparent Green and Red #128

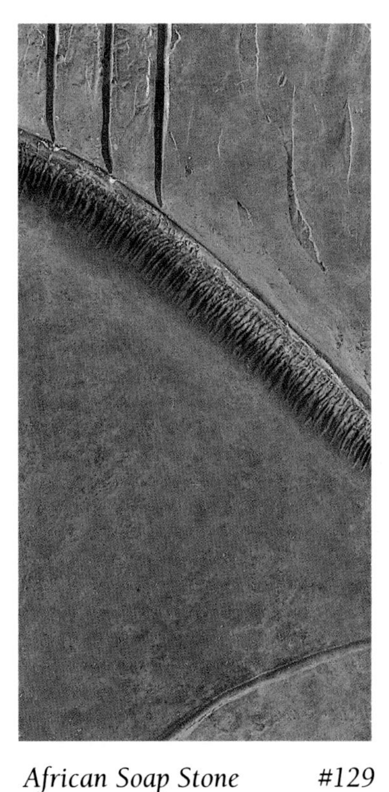

African Soap Stone #129

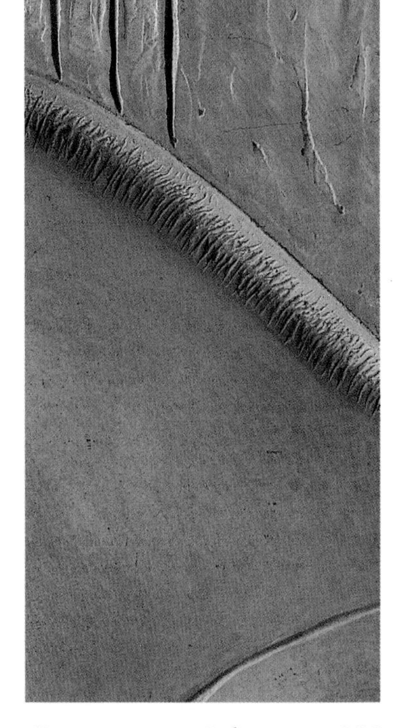

Contemporary Ochre #130

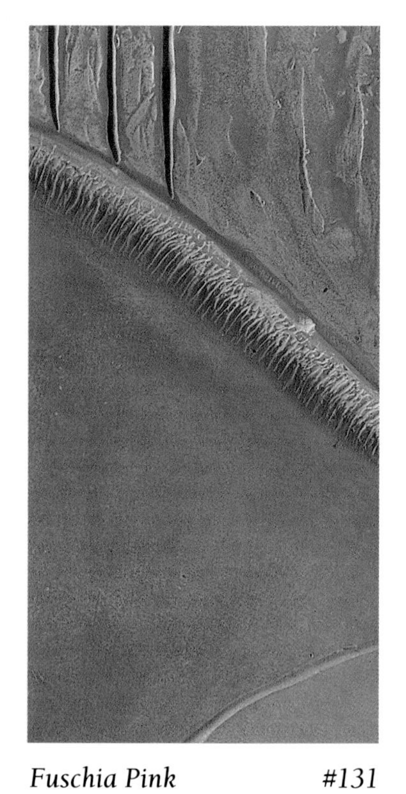

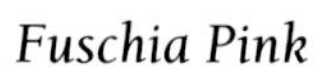

Fuschia Pink #131

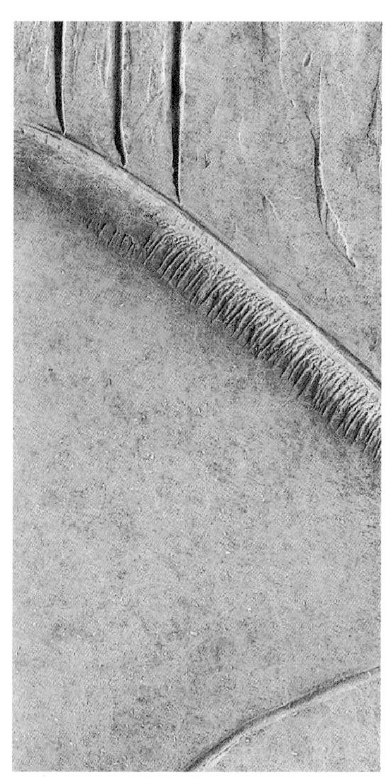

White (Marble White) #132

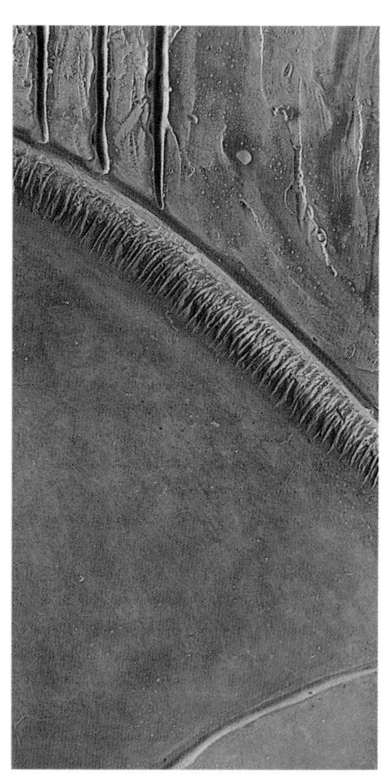

Contemporary Ochre Oxide Wash #133

Arctic Soap Stone #134

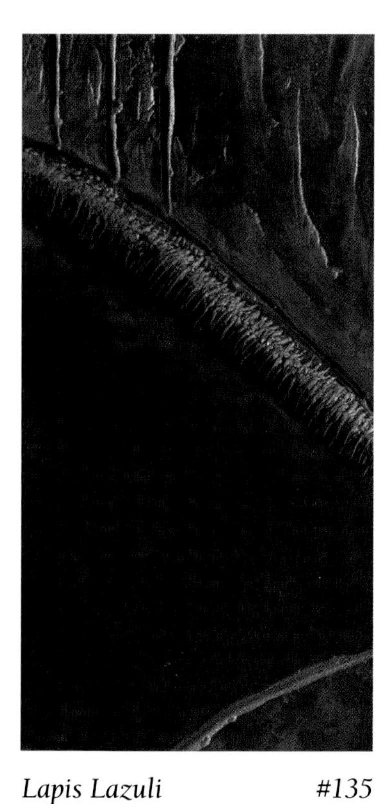

Lapis Lazuli #135

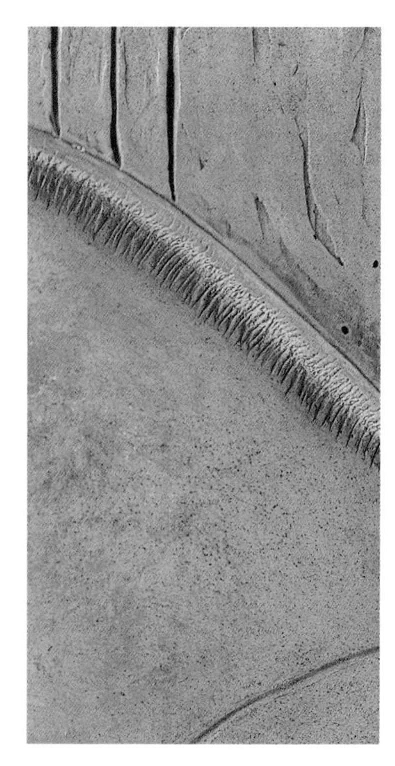

Opaque Yellow #136

Idaho Granite #137

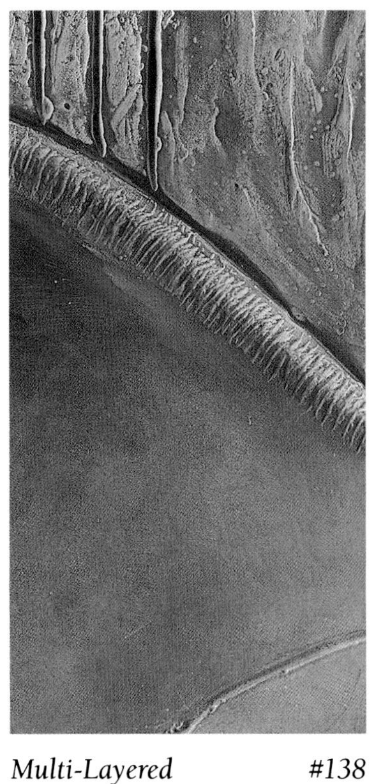

Multi-Layered Oxide Wash #138

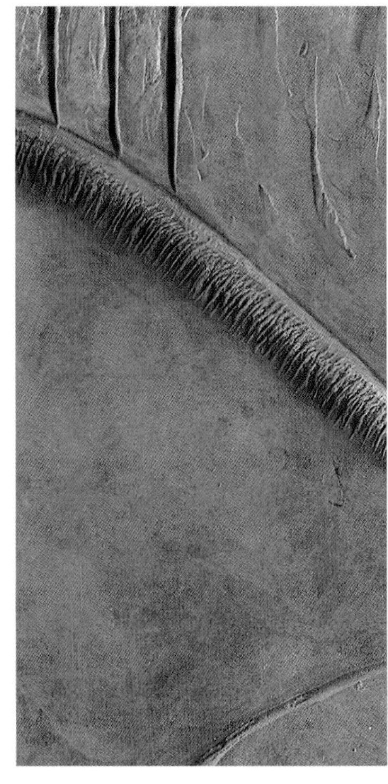

Amber Marble #139

Silver #140

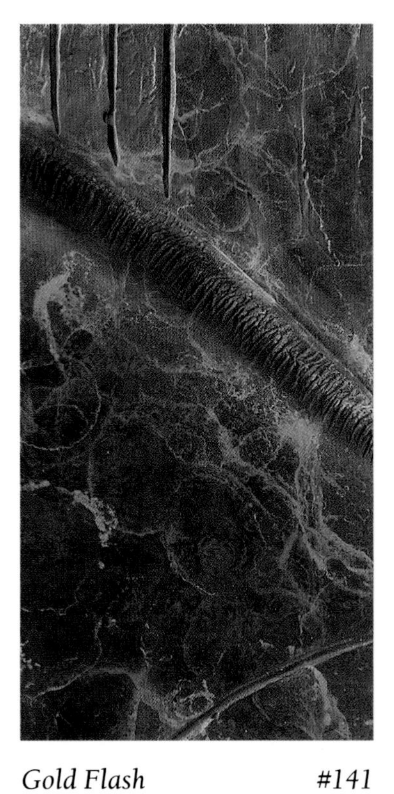

Gold Flash #141

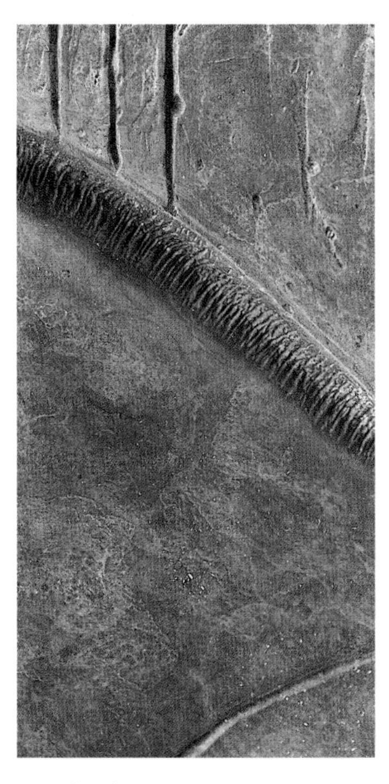

Dutch Blue #142

Rusty Blue Marble #143

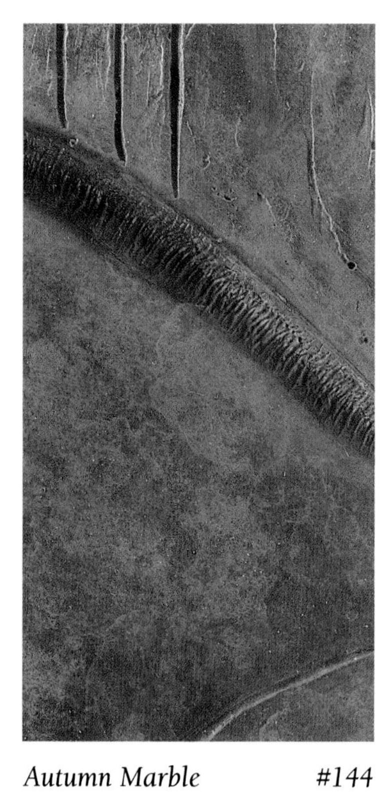

Autumn Marble #144

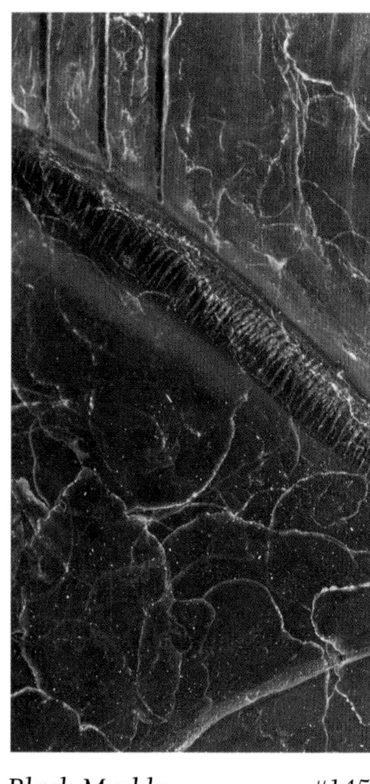

Black Marble #145

Green Marble #146

Gilt Brown #147

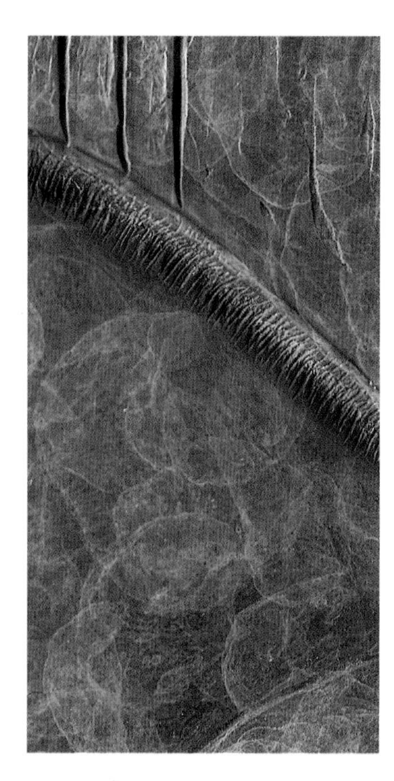

Camouflage #148

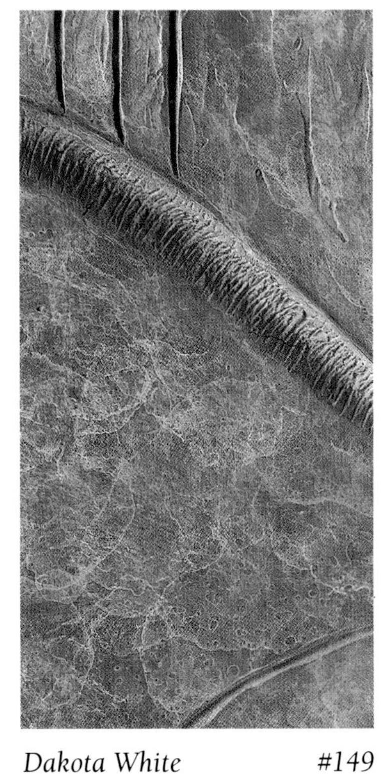

Dakota White Marble #149

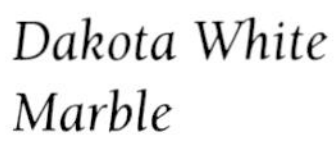

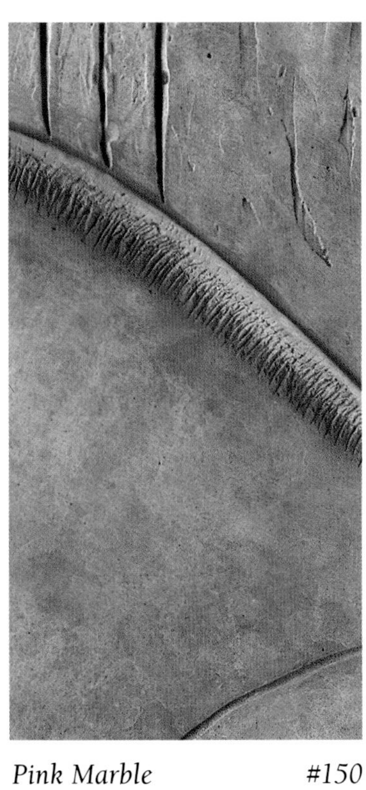

Pink Marble #150

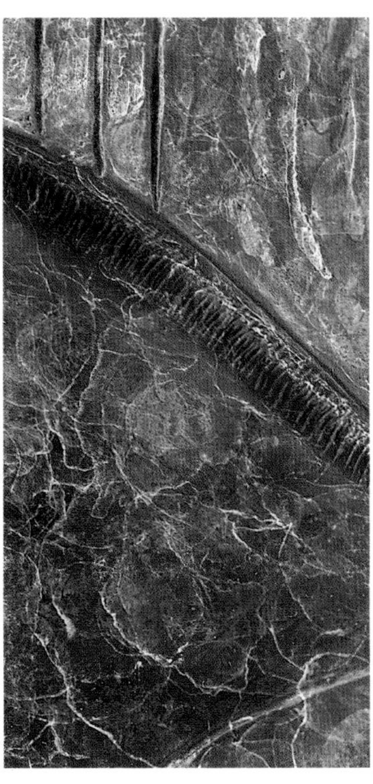

Gray Onyx #151

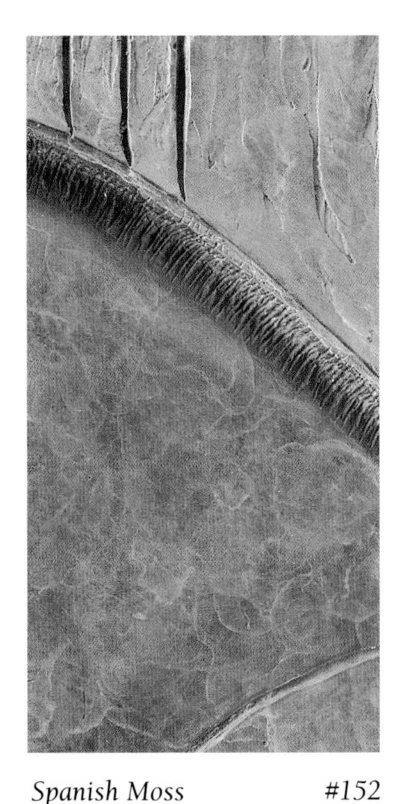

Spanish Moss #152

Roman Brown #153

Red Marble #154

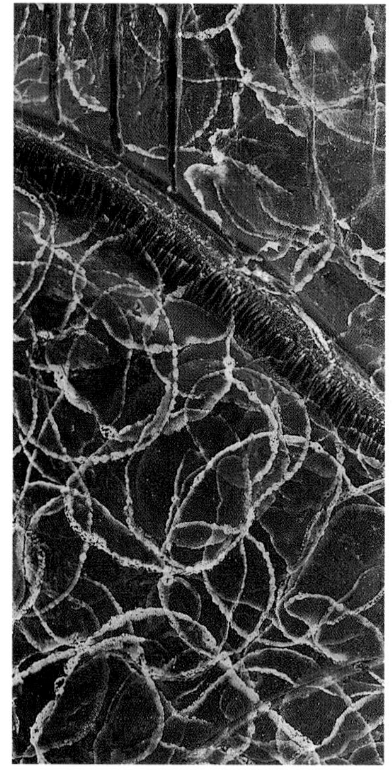

Blue Wave #155

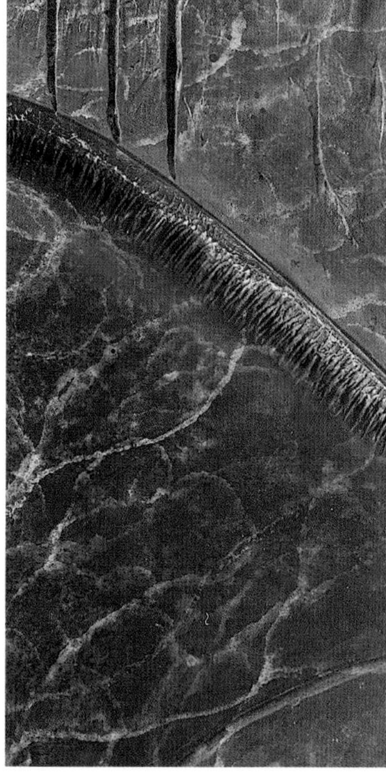

Brown Marble #156

Mars Red #157

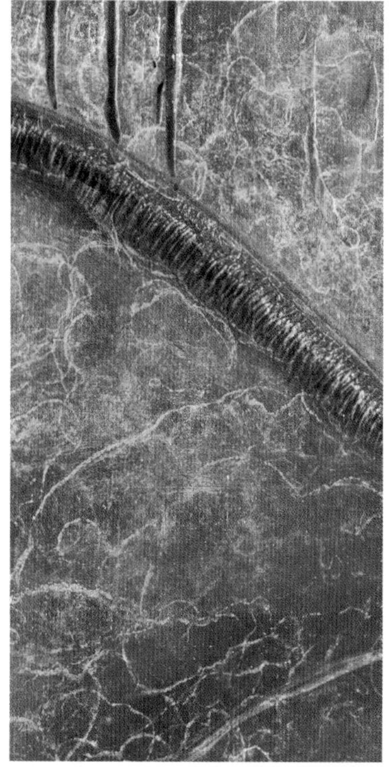

Aqua Marine #158

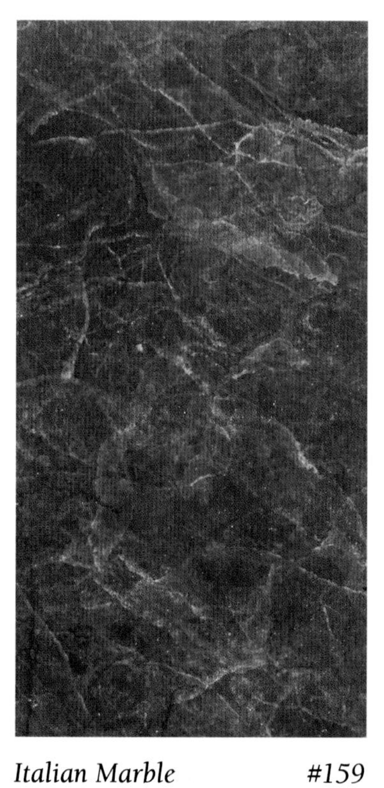

Italian Marble #159

Brown Lace #160

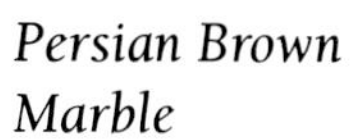

Persian Brown Marble *#161*

Gray Marble *#162*

Blue Nymph *#163*

Gray Granite *#164*

Transparent Brown Granite *#165*

Green Granite *#166*

Red Granite #167

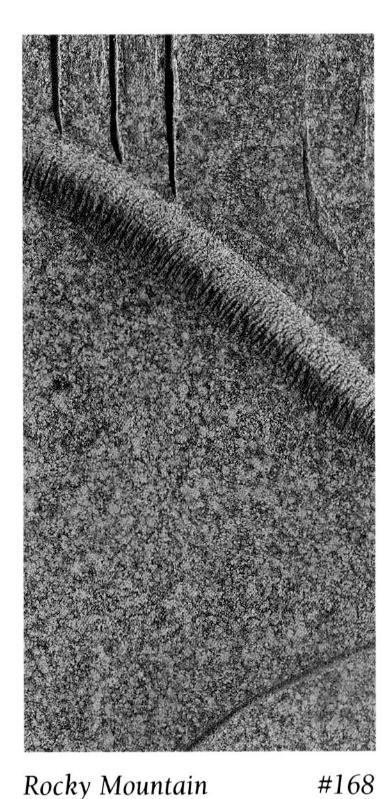

Rocky Mountain Granite #168

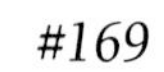

Blue Granite #169

Silver Granite #170

Ancient Green #171

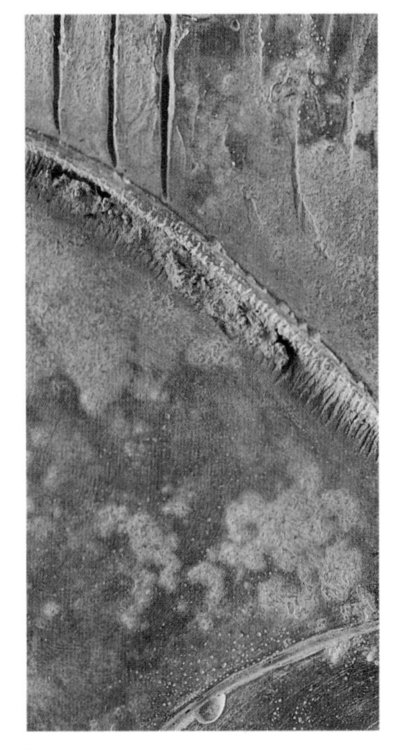

Chiang Green #172

PHOTOGRAPHER: GREGORY STALEY

Artist: Glenna Goodacre
Title: Vietnam Women's Memorial
Patina: #108

PHOTOGRAPHER: JANE HILL

Artist: Glenna Goodacre
Title: Niad
Patina: #104a Variation

Artist: Ann LaRose
Title: Tea for Two
Patina: Multi-Patina

PHOTOGRAPHER: JOE COCA

Artist: Steve Kestrel
Title: Circle of Cranes
Patina: #111

Artist: Steve Kestrel
Title: Desert Solitaire
Patina: #138

PHOTOGRAPHER: JOE COCA

Artist: Tim Cherry
Title: Snake In The Grass
Patina: #141

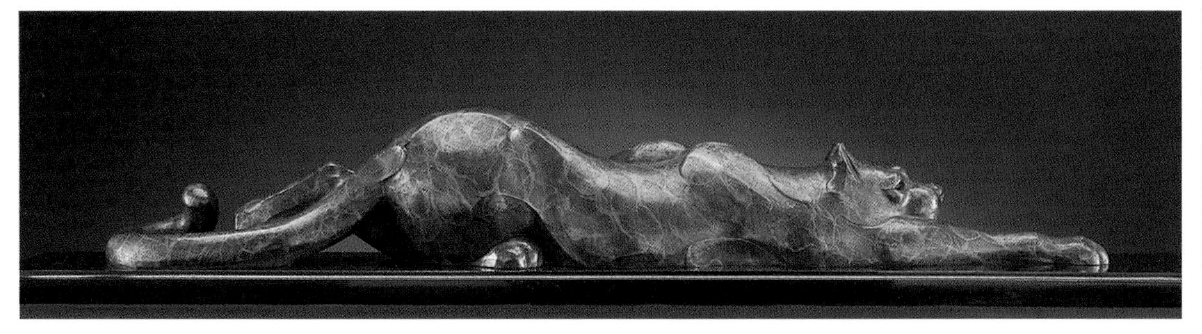

PHOTOGRAPHER: MEL SCHOCKNER

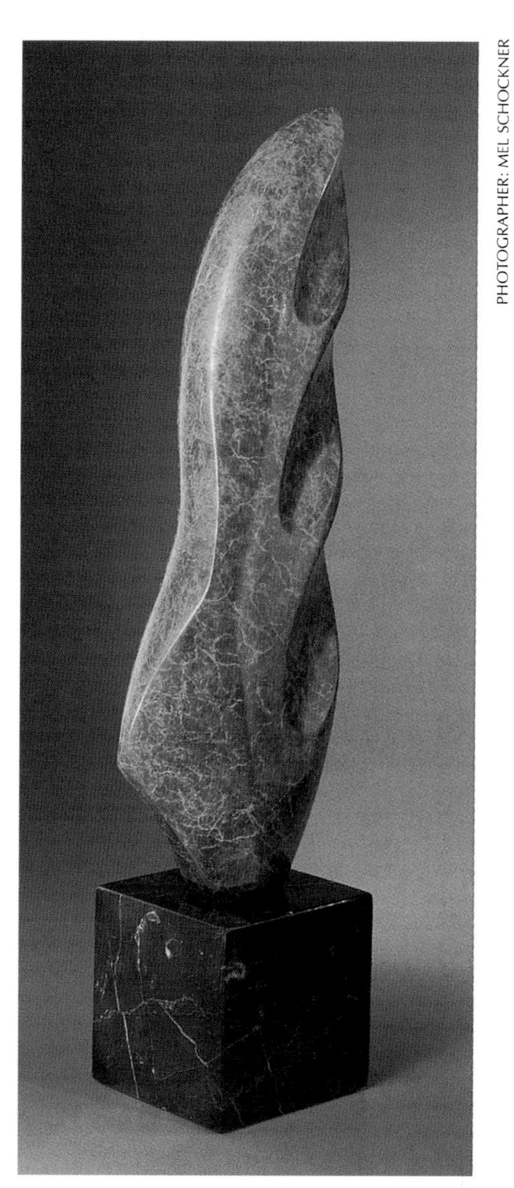

PHOTOGRAPHER: MEL SCHOCKNER

Artist: Mark Leichliter
Title: Rain
Patina: #158

Artist: Kent Ullberg
Title: Tidal Dance
Patina: #114

PHOTOGRAPHER: MEL SCHOCKNER

Artist: Tim Cherry
Title: Arctic Wrap
Patina: #140

PHOTOGRAPHER: MEL SCHOCKNER

Artist: Mark Leichliter
Title: Gaea
Patina: #161

PHOTOGRAPHER: MEL SCHOCKNER

Artist: Rosetta
Title: The Challenge
Patina: #153

PHOTOGRAPHER: MEL SCHOCKNER

Artist: Rosetta
Title: Running Cheetah
Patina: #165

PHOTOGRAPHER: MEL SCHOCKNER

Artist: Richard Greeves
Title: Huron
Patina: #110

PHOTOGRAPHER: MEL SCHOCKNER

Artist: Judy Black
Title: Almost Home
Patina: #124

PHOTOGRAPHER: JOE COCA

Artist: Rosie Sandifer
Title: Study, Flower Girl
Patina: #112

PHOTOGRAPHER: FABRICE

Artist: Jane DeDecker
Title: Cartwheel
Patina: #125

Artist: unknown
Japanese Disc Reproduction
Patina: #109

PHOTOGRAPHER: MEL SCHOCKNER

Recipes

COMMON BASIC APPLICATIONS

1) All liver of sulfur, Birchwood Casey™, and ammonium sulfide mixtures are sprayed onto a cold surface using a plastic squirt bottle.

2) All nitrate mixtures are applied to a hot surface via brush or airbrush.

3) All lacquers are thinned in a 50% solution and are then sprayed onto a warm or cool surface through an airbrush.

4) Only Johnson's Paste Wax™ is applied to a hot surface. All other waxes are applied to a cold surface, usually over a lacquered seal.

CHEMICAL MIXTURES

*** USE DISTILLED WATER FOR ALL MIXTURES ***

Ferric Nitrate Crystals

Weak Solution:	1/4 teaspoon $FeNo_3$ + 8 oz. water
Medium Solution:	1/2 teaspoon $FeNo_3$ + 8 oz. water
Strong Solution:	1 teaspoon $FeNo_3$ + 8 oz. water

Ferric Nitrate Homemade

Weak Solution:	1 tablespoon $FeNo_3$ + 8 oz. water
Strong Solution:	3 tablespoon $FeNo_3$ + 8 oz. water

Cupric Nitrate Crystals

Weak Solution:	1 teaspoon $CuNo_3$ + 1/2 teaspoon $ZnNo_3$ + 8 oz. water
Medium Solution:	2 teaspoon $CuNo_3$ + 1 teaspoon $ZnNo_3$ + 8 oz. water
Strong Solution:	3 teaspoon $CuNo_3$ + 11/2 teaspoon $ZnNo_3$ + 8 oz. water

---

Silver Nitrate Crystals

Weak Solution:	2 to 4 small crystals $AgNo_3$ + 8 oz. water
Medium Solution:	1/4 teaspoon $AgNo_3$ + 8 oz. water
Strong Solution:	1/2 teaspoon $AgNo_3$ + 8 oz. water

Bismuth Nitrate Crystals

Weak Solution:	1/2 teaspoon $BiNo_3$ + 8 oz. water
Medium Solution:	1 teaspoon $BiNo_3$ + 8 oz. water

Oxide Wash

Titanium Oxide:	1 teaspoon TiO_2 + 8 oz. water
Chromium Oxide:	1 teaspoon CrO_2 + 8 oz. water

Sulfurated Potash (Concentrate)

1 thimble size lump or 2 or 3 small chips of K_2S plus 1 quart water

For diluted mixture: 4 tablespoon K_2S + 10 oz. water in squirt bottle

---

Birchwood Casey™ M20 mixture

4oz. Birchwood Casey™ M20 + 4oz. water in squirt bottle

#101 Antique Black

Style Traditional
Technique Spray
Effect Solid opaque black, brown black, gray black

Chemical Mixtures
1) Dilute liver of sulfur mixture
2) Medium ferric nitrate mixture

Surface Preparation
Sandblasted

Application
1) Spray bronze with liver of sulfur solution from bottom to top, until even dark gray is achieved. Rinse with running water.
2) Heat surface slowly, removing all moisture from surface. Continue heating until color change begins to develop.
3) Rub surface to remove excess sulfide residues, leaving an even dark silvery gray. Use "0" steel wool on an untextured surface and a stiff, natural bristled brush on textured areas.
4) Reheat and lightly spray surface with solution of ferric nitrate until basecoat is dark.
5) Hot wax with Johnson's Paste Wax™, or let cool and seal with lacquer, followed by two coats of Trewax™. Allow it to dry, and buff after each coat.

Variations: 101a, 101b
101a) Birchwood Casey™ M20 may be sprayed onto the surface with a 50-50 M20/water solution as a substitute for liver of sulfur. Heat and highlight the same. Use weak cupric nitrate or ferric nitrate solution to spray over base coat. Seal as desired.
101b) For black-black, substitute nitrate sprays with a medium ferric nitrate mixture and 1 tablespoon ferric oxide black. Dab onto reheated hot surface until entire piece is solid black. Use dry brush and sweep back and forth across surface to remove excess black oxides. Seal hot with wax, or cool and seal with lacquer followed by 2 coats of Trewax™. Let dry and buff.

Remarks
Excellent for outdoor exposure. Wears well, but becomes lighter and dustier with age.

#102 Transparent Antique Gold

Style Traditional
Technique Brush
Effect Deep, transparent, mottled golden brown

Chemical Mixtures

1) Medium ferric nitrate mixture
or 1a) Medium homemade ferric nitrate mixture

Surface Preparation

Sand to 220 finish or/and hand sand with #96 Scotch-Brite™ hand-pad. Steel wool and then pumice surface, blow clean.

Application

1) Heat surface until light amber color appears. Dab on ferric nitrate, applying to surface as heated. Work toward an even coat.
2) Wax hot or let cool and seal with lacquer, followed by 2 coats of Trewax™, drying and buffing after each coat.

Variations: 102a

102a) 1/4 to 1/2 teaspoon Potassium dichromate added to one cup of water may be used as a substitute for nitrate mixtures. Effect may be a little orange.

Remarks

Durable outdoor patina if sealed with lacquers. Tends to darken slightly with age.

#103 Antique Gray

Style Traditional
Technique Spray
Effect Gray base with bronze highlight

Chemical Mixture

1) Diluted liver of sulfur mixture

Surface Preparation

Sandblasted

Application

1) Spray liver of sulfur solution over entire piece, achieving even, dark gray.
2) Heat bronze until all moisture is gone from surface.
3) Highlight with #1 medium steel wool or pumice until residues are removed from high points or metal is lightly seen coming through liver base coat.
4) Reheat until bare bronze begins to take on amber coloration.
5) Hot wax or let cool and lacquer, followed by 2 coats of Trewax™, drying and buffing after each coat.

Variations: 103a

103a) Birchwood Casey™ M20 50/50 solution may be substituted for liver of sulfur. Highlight when surface is hot. Continue with recipe.

Remarks

Very durable patina and probably the easiest to apply and maintain.

#104 Old World Green

Style Traditional
Technique Spray / Brush
Effect Dusty gray green or opaque green over gray

Chemical Mixtures

1) Birchwood Casey™ M20 50/50 mixture
2) Strong cupric nitrate mixture plus a few crystals of ferric nitrate or a few drops of homemade ferric nitrate
3) Clean water and a clean round brush (1/4 teaspoon titanium oxide added to water is optional)

Surface Preparation

Sandblasted

Application

1) Spray M20 solution over entire piece until bronze turns even brown-black. Rinse.
2) Heat surface to remove all moisture. Keep heating until slight color change occurs.
3) Gently rub back surface residues using "0" steel wool or a stiff, natural bristle brush. This should result in a soft steel-gray.
4) Reheat, and, using an airbrush, spray on light coating of cupric nitrate-ferric nitrate mixture until first signs of green appears. Keep heating and spraying until even coat of cupric nitrate is visible.
5) Dip clean, round brush into water, and wash surface or quench under running water for a second. The green coloration will become brighter.
6) Reheat, and using a clean brush and water, keep scrubbing piece until light, chalky recessed areas appear. One-fourth teaspoon of titanium oxide may be added to speed up chalky effect.
7) While piece is still hot, gently rub surface with "0" steel wool or use pumice to release cupric nitrate from base coat.
8) Let cool and lacquer, followed by 2 coats of Trewax™ drying and buffing after each coat.

Variations: 104a

104a) Use liver of sulfur instead of Birchwood Casey™ mixture for a base coat. Heat, and, using 1/2 teaspoon of titanium oxide and 1 teaspoon chromium oxide to 8 oz of water, wash surface. Reheat and wash with brush, back and forth until light, dusty green is in recessed areas and gray is on high points. Let cool and seal as in step 8.

Remarks

Very durable patina. Works well for fountains. Watch for signs of dicuprous oxide development.

#105 Opaque Brown

Style Traditional
Technique Brush
Effect Opaque chocolate red-brown to black-brown

Chemical Mixtures

1) Medium ferric nitrate mixture plus 9 crystals sodium thiosulfate

or 1a) Strong homemade ferric nitrate mixture plus 9 crystals sodium thiosulfate

Surface Preparation

Sandblasted (optional)

Application

1) Heat bronze until amber coloration develops. Dab on ferric nitrate mixture, heating and dabbing, until even dark brown develops.
2) Wax hot for dark chocolate brown or let cool and seal with lacquer, followed by 2 coats of Trewax™, drying and buffing after each coat.

Variations: 105a

105a) For a blacker brown, use a liver of sulfur base coat. Then heat and apply ferric nitrate mixture and seal as in step 2.

Remarks

Classic opaque brown, durable for outdoor exposure.

#106 Grecian Blue

Style Traditional
Technique Brush (flat or round) stipple
Effect Opaque light blue stipple over black. Very antique looking.

Chemical Mixtures

1) Birchwood Casey 50/50™ mixture
2) Strong cupric nitrate mixture

Surface Preparation

Sandblasted

Application

1) Spray Birchwood Casey™ solution over cool surface until entire piece is dark brownish-black. Rinse.
2) Heat piece until all signs of moisture are gone and slight color change has begun.
3) Rub smooth surface with "0" steel wool, or use a stiff, natural bristle brush on textured surface to remove brown residue.
4) Reheat surface until hot. Dip brush into cupric nitrate mixture and shake out excess. Carefully stipple over black base coat, heating and stippling, being careful not to scorch cupric as applying, until an even effect is obtained.
5) Quench with running water to help neutralize cupric.
6) Let cool and seal with lacquer, followed by 2 coats of Trewax™, drying and buffing after each coat.

Variations: 106a, 106b

106a) For a green stipple effect, add a few crystals of ferric nitrate into the chemical mixture, or 2 or 3 drops of homemade ferric.

106b) For an ochre stipple, add 1/4 teaspoon ferric nitrate crystals to strong cupric nitrate mixture, or adding 1 to 2 tablespoons of homemade ferric added will give the same results.

Remarks

Very durable patina except when placed outdoors. Specks from stippling seem to darken a bit. Watch for dicuprous oxide development on surface when placed outdoors.

#107 Mottled Turquoise

Style Traditional / Contemporary
Technique Brush
Effect Opaque black veining over solid green to blue green base coat

Chemical Mixtures

1) Birchwood Casey™ 50/50 mixture
2) Strong cupric nitrate mixture
3) Weak ferric nitrate mixture
4) Ferric oxide black on dry palette

Surface Preparation

Sandblasted (optional)

Application

1) Spray Birchwood Casey™ 50/50 mixture on surface until even brownish-black coloration is developed. Rinse.
2) Heat surface until all signs of moisture have disappeared. Keep heating until slight color change begins to develop. Then rub surface with "0" steel wool to remove brown residues, leaving a steel gray.
3) Reheat bronze until hot, then begin dabbing cupric nitrate mixture onto surface. Keep heating and dabbing until solid coat of cupric nitrate is achieved.
4) Quench with running water.
5) Reheat surface carefully until hot. Be careful not to scorch cupric nitrate layers. Lightly load brush with weak ferric nitrate mixture and dab onto dry palette of black oxide, barely picking up any traces of black residue. Then apply to surface in a dabbing motion, creating black veins over solid cupric. Stipple black over dabbing to give a more interesting effect.
6) Let cool and seal with lacquer, followed by 2 coats of Trewax™, drying and buffing after each coat.

Variations: 107a, 107b

107a) For a blacker patina with just a little blue green coming up through the patina, load more black oxide off of the dry palette onto the ferric nitrate brush. Then apply, leaving much blacker opaque areas. Let cool and seal as usual.

107b) When applying cupric nitrate mixture, layer it so as to allow the Birchwood Casey™ basecoat to come through, then continue as usual. This will give a much more interesting effect of depth to the patina.

Remarks

107b Tends to be a much deeper patina than plate 107, due to its layering. This patina is quite durable for indoor use and is somewhat unstable for outdoor exposure. If placed outdoors, check for dicuprous oxide development.

#108 French Brown

Style Traditional
Technique Brush / Spray
Effect Transparent red brown

Chemical Mixtures

1) Dilute liver of sulfur mixture
2) Medium ferric nitrate mixture for brush or spray application

or 2a) Strong homemade ferric nitrate mixture

Surface Preparation

Sandblasted

Application

1) Spray dilute liver of sulfur mixture over surface until an even gray is achieved. Rinse.
2) Highlight surface with #96 Scotch-Brite™ handpad to remove liver residues, rinsing as you go. Then highlight with steel wool to smooth scratches left from Scotch-Brite™ handpad. Steel wool should also be used to remove black residues left in deep recessed areas around eyes and nose in figurative sculpture. Soft brass brushes may be used as well to remove liver residues.
3) Heat slowly and evenly until an amber coloration begins to appear on highlighted surfaces.
4) Spray ferric nitrate mixture on heated surface, heating and spraying, careful not to scorch ferric nitrate. Continue this process until an even reddish coloration has developed on highlighted areas.
5) Wax hot with Johnson's Paste Wax™ or let cool and seal with lacquer, followed by 2 coats of Trewax™, drying and buffing after each coat.

Variations: 108a, 108b, 108c, 108d, 108e

108a) Birchwood Casey™ M20 mixture may be substituted for a highlighted basecoat.

108b) Ammonium sulfide solution may be substituted for highlighted basecoat. Mix 1 teaspoon ammonium sulfide liquid to 8 oz. water and spray as with liver or Birchwood Casey™.

108c) Medium ferric nitrate mixture may be brushed on instead of spraying, as this will give a more antique look. If homemade ferric nitrate is used, a strong mixture may be used as well. Don't brush straight homemade ferric nitrate onto surface, as an opaque effect will be obtained.

108d) By repeated layering of the above applications of ferric nitrate mixtures, a deep burgundy may be achieved.

108e) Darker brown may be obtained by highlighting the base coat with steel wool only. This will leave more liver on the surface which will result in a darker finish. Continue with steps 3 through 5.

Remarks:

This is a great outdoor patina with many variables of coloration. Blasting the surface with a large grit sand prior to patina will give darker results than using 150 to 180 grits, as the deeper and larger the toothing, the more liver residues will be trapped onto the surface.

#109 Chinese Brown

Style Traditional
Technique Brush
Effect Opaque, dusty, antique chocolate brown

Chemical Mixtures

1) Medium ferric nitrate mixture plus 9 crystals sodium thiosulfate

or 1a) Strong homemade ferric nitrate mixture plus 9 crystals sodium thiosulfate

2) Medium bismuth nitrate mixture

3) Clean brush and clean water

Surface Preparation

Sandblasted

Application

1) Heat bronze surface until amber coloration appears. Dab ferric nitrate-sodium thiosulfate mixture onto surface, heating and applying until a dark brown is achieved.
2) Then continue heating, and dab on bismuth nitrate mixture (not much reaction will be seen during this application). Ensure that an even coat has been applied.
3) Wash surface with clean brush loaded with clean water, heating and scrubbing. The bismuth nitrate will immediately begin to become chalky from the water application.
4) Repeat steps 1,2 or 3 if dustier, richer tones are required.
5) Let cool and seal with lacquer, followed by 2 coats of Trewax™, drying and buffing after each coat. Sealing is optional with this patina, but will darken with handling.

Variations: 109a

109a) A titanium oxide wash may be substituted for bismuth nitrate, but the results are somewhat different and not long lasting.

Remarks

If enough layers are applied with this patina, no sealer is required when placed outdoors. Even this patina placed indoors is quite durable without a sealer but tends to darken from handling. Do not wax this patina without a lacquer sealant applied first, as wax may darken and kill much of the dusty appearance. Noticeable color changes from five years of outdoor exposure are minimal. Light greens develop with time, and the patina tends to become more chalky, adding to a nicely aged effect.

#110 Classic Brown

Style Traditional
Technique Brush
Effect From opaque light ochre with black veins to a dark, aged leather look.

Chemical Mixtures

1) Birchwood Casey™ 50/50 mixture
2) Strong cupric nitrate mixture
3) Medium ferric nitrate mixture

or 3a) Weak homemade ferric nitrate mixture

4) Black ferric oxide on dry palette

Surface Preparation

Sandblasted (optional)

Application

1) Spray entire piece with Birchwood Casey™ 50/50 mixture until the entire piece is brownish-black. Wait 30 seconds, then rinse.
2) Heat surface until all moisture is gone and color change begins to develop.
3) Rub smooth surface with "0" steel wool or textured surface with a stiff natural bristle brush to remove brown residues. The basecoat should be a steel gray.
4) Reheat and dab on strong cupric nitrate mixture, continuing to heat and apply until even solid blue-green coat is achieved. (This cupric nitrate layer may be sprayed onto the surface if a more even coat is required.)
5) Quickly quench surface with water to neutralize and set the cupric layer.
6) Reheat and apply layer of medium ferric nitrate mixture or for darker brown, applying three or four layers of medium ferric nitrate. (If using homemade ferric nitrate, use a weak mixture for ochre or a strong mixture for brown.) An even coat is not required if some green is requested here and there.
7) Dab loaded brush with ferric nitrate mixture onto dry palette, just enough to pick up minimal oxide black. Then apply it to the surface in a dabbing fashion, until entire piece is covered.
8) Let cool and seal with lacquer, followed by two coats of Trewax™, drying and buffing after each coat.

Variations: 110a, 110b

110a) This patina can be darkened to almost a solid black by the addition of more black oxide added to the brush as in step 7.

110b) The cupric nitrate layer as well as the ferric nitrate layer may be applied in a mottled fashion, giving greens and browns underneath the oxide black overlay.

Remarks

An excellent antique patina. Medium durability in outdoor exposure; tends to lighten slightly with age. Carbon may be used instead of black oxide in this recipe.

#111 Tortoise Shell

Style Traditional / Contemporary
Technique Brush
Effect Translucent tortoise shell pattern with black over iridescent red-brown. This patina can vary considerably.

Chemical Mixtures

1) Medium ferric nitrate mixture plus 3 crystals sodium thiosulfate

or 1a) Strong homemade ferric nitrate mixture plus 3 crystals sodium thiosulfate

2) Black ferric oxide on dry palette

Surface Preparation

Sand surface to at least a 220 to 320 grit finish. Hand-sand surface with # 96 Scotch-Brite™ handpads followed by #1 medium steel wool, or pumice surface clean with a soft cloth. Blow clean.

Application

1) Heat surface until amber coloration just begins to appear. Dab on ferric nitrate mixture, heating and dabbing until entire surface is a coppery reddish-brown.
2) Load brush with ferric nitrate mixture and touch against oxide black on dry palette, barely picking up any traces of oxide black onto brush.
3) Apply black oxide to surface, heating and dabbing in an irregular pattern until entire surface has a dark, somewhat uneven coat.
4) Let cool and seal with lacquer, followed by two coats of Trewax™, drying and buffing after each coat.

Variations: 111a

111a) A weak solution of ferric nitrate may be used instead of a medium mixture to give more of a golden undertone. Alternating weak and medium ferric nitrate mixture applications may give more interesting results.

Remarks

Excellent patina for outdoors. Rich antique look resembling that of a tortoise shell.

#112 Traditional Ochre

Style Traditional
Technique Brush
Effect Opaque ochre and green

Chemical Mixtures

1) Birchwood Casey™ 50/50 mixture
2) Strong cupric nitrate mixture
3) Medium ferric nitrate mixture

or 3a) Weak homemade ferric nitrate mixture

Surface Preparation

Sandblasted (optional). If not sandblasted, clean surface with #96 Scotch-Brite™ handpads and pumice. Blow clean.

Application

1) Spray Birchwood Casey™ 50/50 mixture onto surface until an even brownish-black is obtained. Rinse.
2) Heat entire surface slowly until all signs of moisture are gone. Continue heating until hot.
3) Clean the brown residues from the bronze surface with #1 medium steel wool or a stiff, natural bristle brush until a steel gray is achieved.
4) Reheat surface and dab on strong cupric mixture, heating and dabbing in a layering fashion, until a somewhat even coat is achieved.
5) Quench with water to neutralize cupric nitrate layer or, using a clean brush with water, heat and scrub surface, neutralizing cupric layer and giving a chalky effect to the greenish-blue layer.
6) Reheat surface slowly and evenly as possible. Then dab medium ferric nitrate mixture onto cupric layer until desired ochre is achieved.
7) Let cool and seal with lacquer, followed by two coats of Trewax™, drying and buffing after each coat.

Variations: 112a, 112b, 112c

112a) During the washing and neutralizing process in step 5, if using a brush and water to neutralize cupric, a pinch of titanium oxide may be added to the cleaning water for an extra chalky underlay.

112b) For a lighter overall coloration, bypass the Birchwood Casey™ base coat. However, doing so makes for a somewhat unstable patina, never to be placed outdoors.

112c) A mottled, light apple or lime green may be achieved quite easily by substituting medium ferric nitrate mixture with weak mixture in step 6.

Remarks

This patina is quite durable indoors and is somewhat unstable outdoors.

#113 Butterscotch

Style Traditional / Contemporary
Technique Brush
Effect Dusty, opaque orange or brown resembling a ferric chloride patina on other bronze alloys

Chemical Mixtures

1) Strong ferric nitrate mixture plus 1 teaspoon titanium oxide

or 1a) Strong, homemade ferric nitrate mixture plus 1 teaspoon titanium oxide

Surface Preparation

Sandblasted (optional). If piece is to be placed outdoors, blasting is essential.

Application

1) Heat bronze surface slowly and evenly until an amber coloration develops.
2) Dab ferric nitrate-titanium oxide mixture onto the surface, heating and dabbing until an even opaque buildup is obtained.
3) Then, using the same brush, sweep the high points of the textured or smooth surface, removing excess oxide, thus polishing the redder undercoat as it appears, and depositing a dusty effect in recessed areas.
4) Steps 2 and 3 need to be done in smaller sections on larger surfaces.
5) Let cool and seal with lacquer, followed by two coats of Trewax™, drying and buffing after each coat.

Variations

None

Remarks

A very durable patina, but darkens for a short time when placed outdoors because, as the wax warms up on a hot surface, it will melt into the patina slightly, causing darker areas. This problem is short lived, however. Maintain this patina for outdoors or indoors with Trewax™ only. Other waxes may darken this patina permanently.

#114 Antique Burgundy

Style Traditional
Technique Brush / Spray
Effect Burgundy base coat with dusty blue recesses

Chemical Mixtures

1) Strong ferric nitrate mixture plus 3 crystals sodium thiosulfate

or 1a) Strong homemade ferric nitrate mixture plus 3 crystals sodium thiosulfate

2) Strong cupric nitrate mixture in airbrush

Surface Preparation

Sand surface to at least 220 grit finish. Then hand-sand with a #96 Scotch-Brite™ handpad.

Application

1) Heat surface evenly until an amber coloration appears.
2) Then dab brush with ferric nitrate mixture onto the surface to achieve a dark burgundy. Heat and apply, repeating until entire surface is coated.
3) Continue heating, and quickly spray strong cupric nitrate mixture over surface. Spray surface until a light blue coloration begins to block out the burgundy undercoat.
4) Let piece begin to cool. While the surface is cooling, use a very fine steel wool and gently rub the surface to carefully remove the light blue from the high points of textured surfaces, exposing the burgundy base coat.
5) Let piece cool and seal with lacquer, followed by two coats of Trewax™, drying and buffing after each coat.

Variations: 114a, 114b, 114c

114a) A substitute for cupric nitrate is to use an oxide wash of titanium oxide and blue dry pigment added to a wet brush loaded with water. Then wipe the surface in order to deposit light blue pigment in recessed areas, resembling the same look as when using cupric nitrate.

114b) Ammonia may be substituted for cupric nitrate mixture. Heat and apply strong ferric nitrate mixture until an even burgundy appears. Let the surface cool. Then lightly spray ammonia over the surface, misting until the first signs of light blue begins to appear. Stop spraying and allow the surface to dry. Then, using a soft cloth or very fine steel wool, remove the light blue from the high points, revealing the burgundy basecoat. Do not seal with lacquer. Instead, use two coats of Trewax™, drying and buffing after each coat.

114c) Add a few ferric nitrate crystals or a few drops of homemade ferric nitrate to the strong cupric nitrate mixture in order to achieve a greener coloration in the recessed areas.

Remarks

Not a very durable patina for outdoors. The cupric nitrate layer is very unstable, tending to change in hue and value. Variation 114b is much more stable but tends to become lighter and bluer as the patina ages. For a more durable finish that will last outdoors, a light blue acrylic mixture may be used over the burgundy base coat and then wiped away with a rag dipped in xylene. This will give a similar look to cupric.

#115 Italian Gold

Style Traditional / Contemporary
Technique Brush
Effect Transparent, mottled, light golden to honey amber color

Chemical Mixtures

1) Weak ferric nitrate mixture

or 1a) Weak homemade ferric nitrate mixture

Surface Preparation

Sand surface to at least 220 finish. A 320 finish will make for a deeper patina. Wipe surface clean with xylene and let dry. Then rub surface with #96 Scotch-Brite™ handpad followed by #1 medium steel wool.

Application

1) Slowly heat surface until a trace of amber coloration appears.
2) Return to the lower back of the piece and begin reheating and dabbing weak ferric nitrate mixture onto the surface, repeating application until a light, golden transparency is obtained.
3) Let piece cool and seal with lacquer, followed by 2 coats of Trewax™, drying and buffing after each coat. This patina may also be hot waxed, but the patina will tend to darken with age.

Variations: 115a

115a) 1/2 teaspoon of potassium dichromate crystals added to 8 oz. of water may be substituted for weak ferric nitrate mixture. Apply with heat, following the same procedure as with ferric nitrate mixture, until an amber coloration is achieved.

Remarks

This patina is somewhat stable, but will darken with age (more so outdoors). Applying two or three coats of lacquer will slow this process, however.

#116 Cherokee Red

Style Traditional / Contemporary
Technique Brush
Effect Opaque, reddish-brown coloration

Chemical Mixtures

1) Medium ferric nitrate mixture plus 1 teaspoon red ferric oxide

or 1a) Strong, homemade ferric nitrate mixture plus 1 teaspoon red ferric oxide

Surface Preparation

Sandblasted surface is recommended but not necessary.

Application

1) Heat surface until light amber coloration appears.
2) Dab ferric nitrate-red ferric oxide mixture onto surface, heating and dabbing, until the entire surface has an even, reddish-brown coloration.
3) Let piece cool and seal with lacquer, followed by two coats of Trewax™, drying and buffing after each coat.

Variations: 116a

116a) This patina may be waxed hot with Johnson's Paste Wax™ for a darker reddish brown.

Remarks

This patina is quite durable, both indoors and out. It is an excellent choice for small areas of accent coloration in multi-patinas, i.e., red bandannas, etc.

#117 *Transparent Gold*

Style Contemporary
Technique Spray
Effect Glossy, transparent yellow gold

Chemical Mixtures

1) Medium ferric nitrate mixture
or 1a) Weak homemade ferric nitrate mixture

Surface Preparation:

Sand surface to a 220 to 320 grit finish. Then clean surface with xylene on a soft rag. Rub surface with a #96 Scotch-Brite™ handpad followed by #1 medium steel wool. Rub finished surface with rottenstone for a glossy clean finish.

Application

1) Heat surface slowly and evenly until signs of amber coloration begin to appear. If moisture from the casting leaves marks on the finished surface, it will need to be rehighlighted dry, with a Scotch-Brite™ handpad and steel wool just before reheating and chemical application.
2) Begin spraying ferric nitrate mixture through an airbrush, until a light, yellowish to golden color is obtained.
3) Let piece cool and seal with lacquer, followed by two coats of Trewax™.

Variations

None

Remarks

A very stable patina, but may darken a bit with age and extensive handling.

#118 *Apple Green*

Style Contemporary / Traditional
Technique Spray
Effect Opaque apple green

Chemical Mixtures

1) Strong cupric nitrate mixture
2) Medium ferric nitrate mixture

Surface Preparation

Sandblasted

Application

1) Heat surface slowly and evenly until an amber coloration appears.
2) Begin spraying cupric nitrate over surface in a layering fashion until a light blue opaque color is obtained. (Be careful not to scorch cooler areas with the torch.)
3) Quench surface with running water to help neutralize cupric nitrate mixture.
4) Slowly and carefully reheat surface until hot. Then spray ferric nitrate mixture over cupric nitrate base coat until an even ochre coloration appears.
5) Wax hot surface with Johnson's Paste Wax™ to seal. This hot wax application will instantly change the ochre coloration achieved to an apple green.

Variations: 118a

118a) For a darker green appearance, use a Birchwood Casey™ base coat under the cupric nitrate layering.

Remarks

This patina is not very stable for outdoor exposure, but works quite well indoors. This patina is much more stable with a Birchwood Casey™ base coat.

#119 Verde Brown

Style Contemporary
Technique Brush / Spray
Effect Rich, copper, transparent high points with blue and green recessed areas

Chemical Mixtures

1) Diluted liver of sulfur mixture
2) Strong cupric nitrate mixture
3) Medium ferric nitrate mixture

Surface Preparation

Sand surface to 320 grit finish. Clean surface with xylene on a soft rag. Then hand sand with a #96 Scotch-Brite™ handpad followed by #1 medium steel wool. Surface should be very glossy.

Application

1) Sporadically spray liver of sulfur over surface, leaving some dark areas and some very light. Rinse and highlight with steel wool to blend.
2) Heat surface until hot, and spray or brush strong cupric nitrate mixture until a thick, light blue coloration appears.
3) Quench piece with running water and, while wet, highlight cupric nitrate from the high points of texture, leaving thick light blue in recessed areas.
4) Reheat surface, occasionally scorching areas of cupric. Keep heating and using a brush, apply ferric nitrate mixture to the high points, allowing overlay onto blue recessed areas. This will give a rich, copper look to the high points and lime and blue colorations to the recessed areas.
5) Let piece cool and seal with lacquer, followed by two coats of Trewax™, drying and buffing after each coat.

Variations: 119a

119a) This patina may be hot waxed to tone down bright coloration.

Remarks

A very unstable patina for outdoor use as dicuprous oxides may develop. A very rich and somewhat uneven patina when used indoors.

#120 Brownish Gray

Style Contemporary / Traditional
Technique Spray
Effect Translucent Gray Brown

Chemical Mixture

1) Diluted liver of sulfur mixture

Surface Preparation

Sandblasted

Application

1) Spray blasted surface with diluted liver of sulfur mixture until the entire piece is gray-black. Rinse.
2) Highlight wet surface with "0" steel wool, rinsing frequently to remove excess steel wool. A paste of pumice and water may also be used instead of steel wool for releasing liver of sulfur residues.
3) Heat surface evenly until all signs of moisture have disappeared. Keep heating slowly and evenly until surface begins to take on a golden brown hue.
4) Wax hot with Johnson's Paste Wax™, or let cool and seal with lacquer, followed by two coats of Trewax™, drying and buffing after each coat.

Variations: 120a, 120b

120a) Birchwood Casey™ 50/50 solution may be substituted for liver of sulfur to darken the surface.

120b) Ammonium sulfide mixture may be substituted for liver of sulfur to darken the surface.

Remarks

The simplest of patinas, and probably the most durable. Great outdoors as well as inside. Tends to darken a bit with age.

#121 Iridescent Red Brown

Style Contemporary / Traditional
Technique Spray
Effect Iridescent transparent golden to red brown with dark gray recesses

Chemical Mixtures

1) Diluted liver of sulfur mixture
or 1a) Birchwood Casey™ 50/50 mixture
2) Medium ferric nitrate mixture
or 2a) Strong, homemade ferric nitrate mixture

Surface Preparation

At least a 220 grit sanded surface that is lightly blasted with 150 to 180 grit aluminum oxide. Then rub piece with a #96 Scotch-Brite™ handpad, followed by #1 medium steel wool.

Application

1) Spray surface with diluted liver of sulfur mixture until an even dark gray is obtained. Rinse.
2) Highlight surface with an #86 or #96 Scotch-Brite™ handpad followed by #1 medium steel wool, removing as much liver residue as possible. A brass brush may be used to remove the gray base coat from deep crevices, etc. Rinse piece frequently during the highlighting process.
3) Heat surface slowly and evenly until an amber coloration begins to appear.
4) Begin spraying the ferric nitrate mixture, reheating and layering until the desired effect is obtained.
5) Wax hot or let cool and seal with lacquer, followed by 2 coats of Trewax™ drying and buffing after each coat.

Variations: 121a (numerous)

121a) A transparent, golden patina may be developed by spraying just one coat of ferric nitrate on the surface. As layers are built up, color will range from gold, to orange, then red, and finally burgundy.

Remarks:

Very durable patina for both indoors and out. Will darken outdoors quickly when hot waxed as a sealer. Therefore, lacquer is always recommended for sealing against indoor as well as outdoor exposures. Many other clear metal sealers may be substituted for lacquer.

#122 Blue Speckle

Style Contemporary
Technique Brush
Effect Light green opaque patterns over a transparent red base coat

Chemical Mixtures

1) Medium ferric nitrate mixture plus 3 crystals sodium thiosulfate

or 1a) Strong, homemade ferric nitrate mixture plus 3 crystals sodium thiosulfate

2) Medium cupric nitrate mixture

Surface Preparation

Sand surface to at least a 220 grit finish—320 is preferred. Wipe surface with xylene on a soft rag or paper towel. Rub surface with a #96 Scotch-Brite™ handpad followed by #1 medium steel wool (optional).

Application

1) Heat surface slowly and evenly until an amber coloration begins to appear.
2) Return to either the lower back or side of the piece and begin dabbing ferric nitrate mixture onto surface, heating and dabbing until an even, rich reflective red coat is obtained.
3) Return to the lower back or side and begin to apply cupric nitrate mixture on the surface in a stippling fashion. (The brush should touch the surface long enough to give a slight marbling or speckle pattern.) Continue heating and applying until the entire surface is covered.
4) Let cool and seal with lacquer, followed by two coats of Trewax™, drying and buffing after each coat.

Variations: 122a

122a) A few crystals of ferric nitrate or a few drops of homemade ferric nitrate concentrate may be mixed into the cupric nitrate mixture in order to achieve a greener pattern over the brown base coat.

Remarks

Somewhat durable indoor patina, but not recommended for outdoor exposure. When the sun heats up the surface, wax coatings will bleed through lacquer coating and darken blue or green cupric patterns.

#123 Moroccan Blue

Style Traditional / Contemporary
Technique Spray / Brush
Effect Mottled blue over black base coat

Chemical Mixtures

1) Birchwood Casey™ 50/50 mixture
2) Medium cupric nitrate mixture

Surface Preparation

Sandblasted

Application

1) Spray cool surface with Birchwood Casey™ 50/50 mixture over entire piece until even brownish-black coating is obtained. Rinse.
2) Heat surface slowly and evenly until all signs of moisture are gone. Continue heating until color change begins to appear.
3) Rub smooth surface with "0" steel wool or textured areas with a stiff, natural bristle brush to remove brown overlay. A dark steel gray will appear.
4) Reheat surface until hot. Then, starting from the lower back or side of the piece, begin brushing cupric nitrate mixture in a dabbing fashion. Keep heating and layering cupric nitrate until entire surface is a light blue. (Be careful not to scorch cupric.)
5) Quench surface with running water to neutralize and set cupric nitrate layers.
6) Let cool and seal with lacquer, followed by 2 coats of Trewax™, drying and buffing after each coat. Sealing this patina is optional if a flat look is requested. However, this patina will darken due to handling.

Variations: 123a, 123b

123a) A few crystals of ferric nitrate or a few drops of homemade ferric nitrate may be added to the cupric nitrate mixture to give more of a green mottled effect.

123b) For a whiter, more powdery blue pattern, add 1/4 teaspoon bismuth nitrate crystals or 1/4 teaspoon titanium oxide to cupric nitrate mixture prior to application.

Remarks

Very durable patina indoors and somewhat unstable outdoors as dicuprous oxides may develop in a reddish-brown, blotchy pattern.

#124 Dusty Copper Oxide Wash

Style Contemporary
Technique Brush
Effect Somewhat translucent copper high points with dusty beige or tan recesses. (Does best on textured surfaces.)

Chemical Mixtures

1) Medium ferric nitrate mixture plus 3 crystals of sodium thiosulfate

or 1a) Strong homemade ferric nitrate plus 3 crystals sodium thiosulfate

2) Titanium oxide wash mixture

Surface Preparation

Sand surface to at least a 220 grit finish (320 grit finish will give deeper results). Wipe surface with xylene on a soft rag or paper towel. Then rub surface with a #96 Scotch-Brite™ handpad followed by #1 medium steel wool.

Application

1) Heat surface with torch slowly until amber coloration develops.
2) Return to the lower back or side of piece and begin reheating and applying ferric nitrate-sodium thiosulfate mixture. Keep heating and applying until the entire surface has a light, transparent copper coloration.
3) Starting from upper back of piece, and working downward, dab titanium oxide mixture, applying a thin white layer over surface. Continue until the entire piece is covered. (Adding too much titanium oxide to the surface will result in an orange color, rather than beige, on recessed areas.)
4) Return to the top of piece and begin dabbing ferric nitrate mixture over titanium oxide in a sweeping or washing motion. This will shift or move the titanium oxide residues into recessed areas, turning them beige and, at the same time, exposing the copper base coat on high points.
5) Let cool and seal with lacquer, followed by 2 coats of Trewax™, drying and buffing after each coat.

Variations

None

Remarks

This patina is quite durable indoors and out, although it must be maintained by cleaning and rewaxing with Trewax™ on a regular basis when placed out in the elements. Larger surfaces may require adding titanium oxide wash and ferric nitrate overlay on smaller areas until entire piece is covered.

#125 *Green Oxide Wash*

Style Contemporary
Technique Brush
Effect Somewhat translucent copper high points with rich, green recesses. (Does best on textured surfaces.)

Chemical Mixtures

1) Medium ferric nitrate mixture plus 3 crystals of sodium thiosulfate

or 1a) Strong, homemade ferric nitrate mixture plus 3 crystals of sodium thiosulfate

2) Titanium oxide wash mixture plus 1 teaspoon Chromium oxide

or 2a) Chromium oxide wash mixture (for darker green)

Surface Preparation

Same as for #124 to achieve a clean, sanded surface.

Application

1) Heat surface slowly until an amber coloration begins to develop.
2) Dab ferric nitrate-sodium thiosulfate mixture onto surface, beginning at the lower back or side of the piece. Working upward, keep heating and applying until entire surface is a transparent copper color.
3) Keep heating, and, starting from the top, dab titanium-chromium oxide mixture onto surface until entire piece has a lime or mint-green coloration.
4) Return to top of piece and begin applying ferric nitrate mixture over titanium oxide, in a sweeping or washing motion. This will shift or move the titanium-chromium oxide mixture into the recessed areas, giving them a rich green coloration and exposing the copper base coat on high points.
5) Repeat steps 3 and 4 if a richer look is requested.
6) Let cool and seal with lacquer, followed by two coats Trewax™, drying and buffing after each coat.

Variations: 125a, 125b

125a) For a darker green in recessed areas, a straight chromium oxide wash mixture is substituted for titanium oxide-chromium oxide mixture in step 3.

125b) Instead of mixing chromium oxide with titanium oxide in mixture, chromium oxide may be placed on a dry palette and then picked up and applied with a brush loaded with titanium oxide wash mixture.

Remarks

This patina is quite durable indoors and out, although it must be maintained by cleaning and rewaxing with Trewax™ on a regular basis when placed out in the elements. Larger surfaces may require working in smaller areas until entire surface is covered.

#126 *Atlantic Blue*

Style Contemporary
Technique Spray
Effect Bare metal to golden high points with light blue recesses. (Textured surface is recommended.)

Chemical Mixtures

1) Strong cupric nitrate mixture

Surface Preparation

Sand surface to a 220 grit finish; 320 grit surface will give a more reflective quality. Wipe surface with xylene on a soft rag or paper towel. Then rub surface with a #96 Scotch-Brite™ handpad, followed by #1 medium steel wool.

Application

1) Heat surface slowly and evenly until an amber coloration begins to develop.
2) Spray cupric nitrate mixture onto surface, heating and spraying until an even, light blue coloration is obtained over entire surface. (Be careful not to scorch cupric.)
3) Quench surface with running water and begin highlighting wet surface with #96 Scotch-Brite™, handpad, rinsing as you go.
4) Reheat surface slowly and carefully to remove excess moisture. Keep heating until a light, rich, golden effect is achieved on high points.
5) Let cool and seal with lacquer, followed by 2 coats of Trewax™, drying and buffing after each coat.

Variations: 126a

126a) For a more interesting look, use a medium cupric nitrate mixture over the surface rather than strong, and then after step 4, hot wax surface. This will give a more transparent green to blue-green effect.

Remarks

Quite durable patina for indoor use but should never be used for outdoor exposure, as dicuprous oxides may develop.

#127 Salmon

Style Contemporary
Technique Brush
Effect Opaque, dusty, pinkish salmon coloration

Chemical Mixtures

1) Strong ferric nitrate mixture plus
   a) 1 teaspoon titanium oxide
   b) 1/2 teaspoon bismuth nitrate crystals
   c) 1/2 teasp. red ferric oxide

or 1a) Strong, homemade ferric nitrate mixture may be substituted for reagent ferric nitrate.

Surface Preparation

Sandblasted (optional). If piece is to be placed outdoors, sandblasting is essential.

Application

1) Heat surface slowly and evenly until amber coloration develops.
2) Return to lower back or side of piece and continue to heat. Begin dabbing ferric nitrate mixture, heating and applying until entire surface is coated.
3) Then, using the same brush, wipe back and forth in a sweeping motion, removing dusty buildup from high points, exposing salmon pink coloration underneath.
4) Let piece cool and seal with lacquer followed by two coats of Trewax™, drying and buffing after each coat.

Variations

None

Remarks

Durable patina both indoors and out. However, if placed outdoors, a regular maintenance program of cleaning and rewaxing should be observed.

#128 Transparent Green and Red

Style Contemporary
Technique Brush / Spray
Effect A bright, transparent green with rich red overtones

Chemical Mixtures

1) Medium cupric nitrate mixture for brush application
or 1a) Strong cupric nitrate mixture for spray application
2) Medium ferric nitrate mixture
or 2a) Strong homemade ferric nitrate mixture

Surface Preparation

Sand surface to at least a 220 finish. A 320 finish is recommended for a more reflective transparency. Wipe surface with xylene on a soft rag, then rub surface with a #96 Scotch-Brite™ handpad, followed by #1 medium steel wool.

Application

1) Heat surface slowly and evenly until an amber coloration begins to appear.
2) Keep heating and begin either brushing or spraying cupric nitrate mixture onto surface, heating and applying until entire surface is covered. If brushing, a thin coat should be gently dabbed on in a layering fashion until a thin, light blue coloration is obtained. This layering should be somewhat translucent in that the metal underneath should be seen through the layering effect. If spraying is requested, a thin, even, light blue, almost completely opaque coloration is achieved.
3) Quench surface with water to help neutralize and set cupric nitrate. Highlighting the high points of texture may be done at this time of rinsing as cupric is much easier to remove from a wet surface than from a dry one. Keep rinsing as you go.
4) Reheat slowly and evenly until surface is once again hot. Then, using a brush, dab ferric nitrate onto the surface on high points and anywhere else that a translucent red or brown is wanted. Lightly brush ferric nitrate over all blue surface to turn the blue to a light, greenish ochre.
5) Wax hot surface with Johnson's Paste Wax™. When this patina is hot waxed, the green undercoat is transformed from an opaque to a transparent, light, lustrous green with reddish-brown and golden high points or patches. Let piece cool and buff.

Variations: 128a

128a) Liver of sulfur may be dabbed here and there prior to heating the bronze for cupric application. The liver may then be highlighted for a darker recessed green. Then continue with steps 1 through 5.

Remarks

Very rich and lustrous patina that is quite durable indoors and very unstable outdoors. Must watch for dicuprous oxide development. This is one of a handful of hot waxed patinas listed in this book

#129 *African Soap Stone*

Style Contemporary
Technique Brush / Spray
Effect Light brown speckle over dark green mottled base coat

Chemical Mixtures

1) Birchwood Casey™ 50/50 mixture
2) Strong cupric nitrate mixture
3) Chromium oxide on dry palette
4) Strong ferric nitrate mixture plus 1/2 teaspoon titanium oxide

or 4a) Strong homemade ferric nitrate mixture plus 1/2 teaspoon titanium oxide

Surface Preparation

Sandblasted

Application

1) Spray Birchwood Casey™ 50/50 mixture onto cool bronze surface until an even, brownish-black is obtained. Rinse.
2) Heat surface slowly and evenly until all signs of moisture have disappeared. Keep heating until slight color change appears.
3) Rub smooth surface with #1 medium steel wool, and textured areas with a stiff, natural bristle brush, until all brown residues are removed, revealing a deep, steel gray base coat.
4) Reheat surface. Dip brush into cupric nitrate mixture and then pick up just a trace of chromium oxide from dry palette. Apply to surface, heating and dabbing until a green mottled effect is achieved.
5) Quench surface with running water to help neutralize and set cupric.
6) Reheat surface and dab on ferric nitrate-titanium oxide mixture in a stippling fashion over cupric nitrate-chromium oxide layer. Heat and stipple until entire surface is covered. The end result should be a brown stipple over green stipple over Birchwood Casey™ base coat.
7) Let cool and seal with lacquer, followed by two coats of Trewax™, drying and buffing after each coat.

Variations

None

Remarks

Excellent indoor patina and tends to change little with outdoor exposure. However, do watch for dicuprous oxide development.

#130 Contemporary Ochre

Style Contemporary
Technique Spray
Effect Even, opaque, yellow ochre

Chemical Mixtures
1) Birchwood Casey™ 50/50 mixture
2) Strong cupric nitrate mixture
3) Medium ferric nitrate mixture
or 3a) Weak homemade ferric nitrate mixture

Surface Preparation
Sandblasted

Application
1) Spray Birchwood Casey™ 50/50 mixture onto cool surface until an even brownish-black coloration is obtained. Rinse.
2) Heat surface slowly and evenly until color change begins to appear.
3) Rub smooth surface with #1 medium steel wool and textured areas with a stiff, natural bristle brush to remove brown, exposing a dark, steel gray.
4) Reheat surface slowly and evenly, then spray cupric nitrate solution over surface. Keep heating and spraying until a solid, light blue color is achieved.
5) Quench with water to help neutralize and set cupric layer. (The blue coloration may become brighter when rinsed.)
6) Reheat surface slowly and evenly, and when hot, spray ferric nitrate mixture over cupric layer, heating and spraying as evenly as possible until a yellow ochre is achieved.
7) Let cool and seal with lacquer, followed by two coats of Trewax™, drying and buffing after each coat.

Variations
None

Remarks
Durable patina for indoor use, but unstable outdoors. (May become quite blotchy due to sun exposure on wax finish and red dicuprous oxide formation.)

#131 Fuchsia Pink

Style Contemporary
Technique Brush
Effect A bright, opaque, dusty fuchsia pink

Chemical Mixtures

1) Medium ferric nitrate mixture plus
   a) 1 teaspoon titanium oxide
   b) 1/2 teaspoon red ferric oxide
   c) 1/2 teaspoon bismuth nitrate crystals

or 1a) A weak homemade ferric nitrate mixture may be substituted for crystal ferric nitrate

Surface Preparation

Sandblasted

Application

1) Heat entire surface slowly and evenly until amber coloration appears.
2) Return to lower back or side of piece and concentrate on heating and applying ferric nitrate mixture until an even pink coloration is obtained.
3) Then, using same brush, wipe back and forth in a sweeping motion to remove dusty deposits from high points, leaving residues in recesses.
4) Let cool and then seal with lacquer, followed by two coats of Trewax™, drying and buffing after each coat.

Variations: 131a

131a) For a hotter pink in recessed areas: after piece is sealed with lacquer, apply white shoe wax on a brush dipped into dry ferric oxide red from a dry palette to the surface, working this pink wax mixture down into recesses. Wipe excess wax from surface immediately, then apply one coat of Trewax™, being careful not to shift pink wax layer. Let dry and buff.

Remarks

Quite durable patina indoors or out. A very hot and bright patina that may be overpowering on large surfaces. This patina is better suited for smaller bronzes or select areas in multi-patinas.

#132 White (Marble White)

Style Contemporary
Technique Brush
Effect Opaque solid white to white marbling (depending on layers and amount applied)

Chemical Mixtures

1) Medium bismuth nitrate mixture plus
   a) 1 teaspoon titanium oxide
   b) 1/2 teaspoon stannic oxide (optional)

NOTE: Prior to use, allow chemical mixture to set for 48 hours, stirring occasionally.

Surface Preparation

Sandblasted

Application

1) Heat surface until an amber coloration is developed.
2) Return to lower back or side of piece and, while heating, apply white bismuth nitrate mixture to surface in a dabbing fashion. Continue heating and applying until an even, solid or marble-layered look is obtained.
3) Quench with running water to neutralize and set bismuth. If any yellowing developed during application, it will probably return to white when quenched.
4) Reheat surface slowly and carefully to remove moisture from patina.
5) Let cool and seal with lacquer, followed by 2 coats of Trewax™, drying and buffing after each coat.

Variations: 132a

132a) This patina is used commonly on such bronzes of animals as polar bears and white egrets. However, since this patina is quite bright for such objects and animals such as polar bears are not pure white, certain steps should be taken to tone down or soften this effect. After the surface has been whitened and quenched, carefully reheat surface and apply a quick spray of medium ferric nitrate mixture—just enough to yellow the white surface. A weak solution may be used as well, but with greater care. Then, while heating piece, dip brush into white bismuth-titanium-stannic oxide mixture and, after shaking excess from bristles, carefully sweep brush back and forth across textured surface, depositing white on high points of texture. This will give depth to an otherwise solid white effect, and a softer look to white feathered areas of birds.

Remarks

Very durable for indoor use, but may tend to turn greener with outdoor exposure unless well sealed with three or four coats of lacquer. White patinas may still become dirty outdoors due to dust and rain deposits. Indoors, white patinas may become soiled and stained from handling. Therefore, it is recommended to handle white patinas as little as possible.

#133 Contemporary Ochre Oxide Wash

Style Contemporary
Technique Brush
Effect Rich, mostly opaque, deep ochre with occasional copper high points in texture

Chemical Mixtures

1) Medium ferric nitrate mixture plus 3 crystals of sodium thiosulfate

or 1a) Strong homemade ferric nitrate mixture plus 3 crystals sodium thiosulfate

2) Titanium oxide wash mixture

Surface Preparation

Sandblasted 220 grit finish. (Use 180 grit aluminum oxide only as larger grits will hold too much oxide.) Then use #1 medium steel wool and gently rub high points of texture to a soft shine.

Application

1) Heat surface until amber coloration begins to develop.
2) Return to lower back or side of piece and begin applying ferric nitrate-sodium thiosulfate mixture. Continue heating and dabbing until a dark, rich copper color appears on high points and a flat brown is developed on the blasted surface.
3) Dab titanium oxide wash onto surface in a pattern or solid effect, whichever is desired. Continue heating and dabbing until entire piece is almost white.
4) Start from the top and, working downward, apply ferric nitrate-sodium thiosulfate mixture over titanium oxide layer to achieve an ochre-beige coloration.
5) Repeat steps 3 and 4 until a rich deep ochre is achieved.
6) Let cool and seal with lacquer, followed by two coats of Trewax™, drying and buffing after each coat.

Variations

None

Remarks

This patina is very durable indoors or outdoors. Ensure that at least two or three coats of lacquer are applied to the surface if piece is to be installed in an outdoor setting.

#134 *Arctic Soap Stone*

Style Contemporary
Technique Brush
Effect Deep patina of soft, light green with brown or beige speckled areas

Chemical Mixtures

1) Strong cupric nitrate mixture plus a few crystals ferric nitrate (or a few drops homemade ferric nitrate)
2) Medium ferric nitrate mixture

or 2a) Strong homemade ferric nitrate mixture

3) Titanium oxide wash mixture

Surface Preparation

Sandblasted

Application

1) Heat surface slowly and evenly until amber coloration appears.
2) Return to lower back or side of piece and continue heating while applying cupric nitrate mixture in a stippling fashion. This stippling should be somewhat layered, if possible, leaving areas of bare bronze, peaking up through the cupric layers.
3) Quench surface with running water to help neutralize and set cupric.
4) Slowly and carefully reheat surface and dab ferric nitrate here and there over green cupric-ferric base coat.
5) Keep heating and apply titanium oxide wash over entire surface until piece is almost white.
6) Let piece cool and seal with lacquer. The lacquer seal will cause the white overcoat to almost disappear completely. After seal has dried, apply two coats of Trewax™, drying and buffing after each coat.

Variations: 134a

134a) If too much white disappeared when sealed, white shoe wax can be brushed over the surface and gently wiped back, then allowed to dry and buff. Follow with one coat of Trewax™, allowing to dry and then buff.

Remarks

Beautiful patina for indoor use. Should not be used for outdoor purposes as dicuprous oxides may develop. If used outdoors, ensure that Birchwood Casey™ 50/50 mixture is used as a base coat.

#135 Lapis Lazuli

Style Contemporary
Technique Brush / Spray
Effect Opaque, deep dark blue and green mottled appearance

Chemical Mixtures

1) Birchwood Casey™ 50/50 mixture
2) Medium cupric nitrate mixture
3) Dark blue dry pigment of ferriferro-cyanide (Prussian Blue)
   Windsor blue pigment or most other dark blue pigment on dry palette

Surface Preparation

Sandblasted

Application

1) Spray Birchwood Casey™ 50/50 mixture over entire piece until surface has brownish-black coloration. Rinse.
2) Heat piece to remove all moisture from surface. Continue heating until slight color change begins to develop. Then rub smooth surface with #1 medium steel wool or use a stiff, natural bristle brush on textured areas to remove brown reside, leaving a blackish, steel gray base coat.
3) Reheat surface and dab loaded brush with cupric nitrate onto dry palette, picking up a good amount of dry pigment. Then apply to surface in a stippling fashion. Not much coloration will appear. It will mostly be a dark iridescent blue-black. This patina should be layered many times to ensure deep even coverage.
4) Quench surface with water; bright coloration should appear immediately.
5) Reheat surface slowly and evenly to remove surface moisture. (If color is not dark or blue enough, reheat and repeat steps 3 and 4, until desired effect is obtained.)
6) Let piece cool and seal with lacquer, followed by two coats of Trewax™, drying and buffing after each coat.

Variations

None

Remarks

Very durable patina for indoor use. Somewhat stable outdoors but lightens as it ages, due to dust and water deposits. Watch for dicuprous oxide development.

#136 *Opaque Yellow*

Style Contemporary
Technique Brush
Effect Opaque, light dusty yellow

Chemical Mixtures

1) Medium bismuth nitrate mixture plus:
   a) 1/2 teaspoon titanium oxide
   b) 1/4 teaspoon ferric nitrate crystals (or 2 teaspoons homemade ferric concentrate)

Surface Preparation

Sandblasted

Application

1) Heat surface slowly and evenly until amber coloration begins to appear.
2) Then return to the back or side of the piece and begin heating and dabbing, in a layering fashion, until entire piece is covered. When mixture first goes onto the surface, it will be almost white, but as heat and layering continues, the yellow will become stronger.
3) Using the same brush, wipe the high points of texture back and forth in a sweeping fashion, removing excess oxides and exposing a light yellow.
4) Let cool and seal with lacquer, followed by 2 coats of Trewax™, drying and buffing after each coat.

Variations: 136a

136a) Spray piece with Birchwood Casey™ 50/50 solution until entire surface is brownish-black. Heat surface until hot and then use steel wool on smooth surfaces, or use a stiff, natural bristle brush on textured areas to remove brown residues, exposing a great steel gray base coat. Reheat and dab mixture onto surface—applying brush by gently laying bristles toward one side. This will allow the chemical mixture to flow off the brush, causing a somewhat opaque circular ring with a foggy or cloudy center. Overlapping this application and stippling here and there results in a great beige to almond white marbling over a dark gray base coat. Seal as usual.

#137 *Idaho Granite*

Style Contemporary / Traditional
Technique Brush / Spray
Effect Dark green, large grained granite on smooth surfaces and antique dark green traditional aged patina on textured surfaces

Chemical Mixtures

1) Birchwood Casey™ 50/50 mixture
2) Medium cupric nitrate mixture
3) Chromium oxide on dry palette

Surface Preparation

Sandblasted

Application

1) Spray surface evenly with Birchwood Casey™ 50/50 solution until entire piece is brownish-black. Rinse.
2) Heat surface to remove all moisture and until color change begins to develop. Piece will then be hot.
3) Gently rub smooth surface with #1 medium steel wool or use a stiff, natural bristle brush to remove brown residues from textured areas, exposing a dark steel gray base coat.
4) Reheat surface from the back or side. Dab brush into cupric nitrate mixture and then onto a dry palette of chromium oxide, barely picking up any pigment. Then apply in a stippling fashion over hot surface, reheating and applying in layers until entire surface is covered.
5) Quench surface with running water to neutralize and set the cupric.
6) Reheat the surface slowly and evenly until all signs of moisture are gone.
7) Let cool and seal with lacquer, followed by two coats of Trewax™, drying and buffing after each coat.

Variations: 137a

137a) On the patina plate, the lower part of the plate has a titanium oxide wash over it and then sealed. This gives a whiter, lighter green look to this granite patina.

Remarks

Very durable patina indoors and somewhat unstable outdoors. Watch for dicuprous oxide development if placed out into the elements.

#138 *Multi-Layered Oxide Wash*

Style Contemporary
Technique Brush
Effect Layered, almost completely solid dusty beige

Chemical Mixtures

1) Medium ferric nitrate mixture plus 3 crystals of sodium thiosulfate

or 1a) Strong homemade ferric nitrate mixture plus 3 crystals sodium thiosulfate

2) Titanium oxide wash mixture

Surface Preparation

Sandblasted with 150 to 180 grit aluminum oxide. Then use #1 medium steel wool and gently rub back any high points where copper base coat will come through the otherwise opaque patina.

Application

1) Heat surface until amber coloration begins to develop.
2) Return to lower back or side of piece and begin applying ferric nitrate-sodium thiosulfate mixture. Continue heating and applying until dark, reddish-brown base coat is obtained.
3) Dab titanium oxide wash onto hot surface, heating and dabbing until entire surface is covered. It should be almost a solid white.
4) Start from top and working downward, continue heating and dab ferric nitrate-sodium thiosulfate mixture onto surface, sandwiching the white oxide wash between the two layers of ferric nitrate-sodium thiosulfate.
5) Repeat steps 3 and 4 twice.
6) The last layer of patina should be a thin layer of titanium oxide wash not turning the surface white, but a lighter beige.
7) Let cool and seal with lacquer, followed by two coats of Trewax™, drying and buffing after each coat.

Variations: 138a

138a) For a warmer coloration with a slightly richer green effect, add 1/2 teaspoon of chromium oxide to the titanium oxide wash mixture. Follow the recipe application until final color desired is achieved.

Remarks

A very durable patina indoors and out, although the life span of this patina is much shorter outdoors than other oxide washes. (This is due to the amount of layering.)

#139 Amber Marble

Style Contemporary
Technique Brush (round and flat)
Effect Rich, light amber and ochre marbling in layers

Chemical Mixtures

1) Medium ferric nitrate mixture plus 3 crystals of sodium thiosulfate

or 1a) Strong homemade ferric nitrate mixture plus 3 crystals sodium thiosulfate

2) Weak bismuth nitrate mixture plus 1/2 teaspoon titanium oxide and a few crystals of ferric nitrate (or 1 tablespoon of homemade ferric nitrate concentrate)

Surface Preparation

Sandblasted

Application

1) Heat surface until amber coloration begins to develop.
2) Return to lower back or side of piece and, using a round brush, begin dabbing ferric nitrate-sodium thiosulfate mixture onto surface. Keep heating and applying, working upward until entire surface has a dark, reddish-brown base coat.
3) Keep heating and return to back or side of piece. Dip flat chip brush into bismuth nitrate solution and barely push or rest tips of bristles against the surface. The chemical mixture should be pulled from the brush and deposited in a ringing or circular effect around the point of bristle contact. Keep heating and applying, overlaying these circular layers and clouding over the brown base coat.
4) Return to ferric nitrate-sodium thiosulfate mixture and apply one thin coat over the bismuth marbling patterns, to change the whitish beige coloration to a warm amber or orange.
5) Repeat steps 3 and 4. As each layer is applied, the patina will become lighter and deeper. (Subsequent layers may be needed until desired effect is obtained.)
6) Let piece cool and seal with lacquer, followed by two coats of Trewax™, drying and buffing after each coat.

Variations

None

Remarks

Very durable patina but may darken with age due to overhandling. This patina is not recommended for outdoor exposure as it will tend to take on a greenish cast. (If this patina is destined for outdoor use, steps 3 and 4 may need to be repeated four to five times in order to compensate for the thicker coats of lacquer required. These thick coats will otherwise darken this patina.

#140 Silver

Style Contemporary
Technique Brush
Effect Bright reflective silver effect, resembling that of silver plating

Chemical Mixtures

1) Birchwood Casey™ 50/50 mixture
or 1a) Dilute liver of sulfur mixture
2) Medium silver nitrate mixture

Surface Preparation

Sand surface to at least a 220, preferably a 320 grit finish. Wipe surface clean with xylene on a clean soft rag or paper towel. Hand rub with a #96 Scotch-Brite™ handpad, followed by either a #1 medium steel wool or rottenstone on a soft rag. Blow clean.

Application

1) Spray surface with either Birchwood Casey™ 50/50 mixture or dilute liver of sulfur mixture until entire surface is dark gray or brownish-black. Rinse with running water.
2) Heat surface until all signs of moisture have disappeared. Keep heating until hot (or slight color change begins to develop).
3) Rub hot surface with "0" steel wool on smooth surface or a stiff, natural bristle brush on textured areas, to remove brown overcoat on Birchwood Casey™ or blackish oxide residues from liver of sulfur. In both results, a dark, steel gray should appear.
4) Reheat surface until hot and begin dabbing silver nitrate mixture, heating and dabbing until entire surface has a soft whitish coloration.
5) Rub surface with "0" steel wool to remove whitish buildup, exposing a bright metallic silver.
6) Repeat steps 4 and 5 if desired until requested effect is obtained.
7) Let cool and seal with lacquer, followed by two coats of Trewax™, drying and buffing after each coat.

Variations: 140a (numerous)

140a) Although the plate shows a bright metallic silver, the surface may be left a dusty cream color. Silver can also be applied to take advantage of the slight dark ringing or stipple patterns that result from brush application. If smaller rings or "pebbling" is requested, this mixture can be sprayed through a squirt bottle, in a spattering fashion, and then rubbed back with steel wool.

140b) If more of a matte gray is requested, either brush or spray silver nitrate mixture onto a sandblasted surface. This may give more of a lead finish.

140c) A pewter finish may be obtained by antiquing a bright metallic silver finish with carbon or black ferric oxide after a lacquer finish. The black oxide or carbon is mixed with Johnson's Paste Wax™ and brushed onto the surface and into textured areas. Then the excess is wiped away immediately. This will darken the overall feel of an antique silver, pushing the end result into more of a pewter finish.

Remarks

This is a very durable patina and can be used both indoors or out. However, keep in mind that it is silver and without continuous maintenance, outdoor exposure will tend to darken this patina.

Care should be taken when deciding on silver nitrate for a finished patina as it can be quite metallic and somewhat overpowering. It is suggested more for smaller pieces and accents in multi-patinas.

#141 Gold Flash

Style Contemporary
Technique Brush
Effect Bright metallic patterns over a darker base coat

Chemical Mixtures

1) Weak ferric nitrate mixture plus 2 to 3 small crystals of silver nitrate

Surface Preparation

Sand surface to a 320 grit finish. Wipe with xylene on soft rag or paper towel. Then rub surface with a #96 Scotch-Brite™ handpad followed by #1 medium steel wool or rottenstone. Blow clean. Surface should have a highly reflective satin polish.

Application

1) Heat surface until a very light amber coloration just begins to appear.
2) Dip brush into silver nitrate-ferric nitrate mixture and then lay bristles against surface, pulling solution from brush and onto surface in a ringing deposit around the bristle contact. Keep heating and repeat this ringing or circular pattern, overlapping these patterns until entire surface is coated. The loaded brush may also be shaken over the surface causing a wonderful spattering effect.
3) Let piece cool and seal with lacquer, followed by two coats of Trewax™, drying and buffing after each coat.

Variations: 141a, 141b

141a) For redder veins or flash on the surface, a few more crystals of ferric nitrate may be added to the solution prior to application.

141b) For an interesting effect of green flashing, a weak cupric nitrate mixture may be substituted for ferric nitrate. Apply in the same fashion and seal accordingly.

Remarks

This is a very interesting patina but can quite easily be distracting from the piece on which it is applied. This patina is highly recommended for smooth bronzes of simple form. Otherwise, this patina may overpower many realistic pieces, causing a very commercial look.

#142 Dutch Blue

Style Contemporary
Technique Brush
Effect Blue marbling pattern. (May also be applied for a solid blue.)

Chemical Mixtures

1) Medium bismuth nitrate mixture
2) Prussian or Windsor blue dry pigment on dry palette

Surface Preparation

Sandblasted. Then rub surface with #1 medium steel wool.

Application

1) Heat surface slowly and evenly until an amber coloration begins to appear.
2) Return to lower back or side of piece and continue heating until hot. Dab brush loaded with bismuth nitrate mixture onto palette, picking up a small amount of dark blue pigment. Then dab loaded brush onto surface, heating and dabbing in a layering fashion. Repeated buildup of pigmented bismuth nitrate can result in a completely opaque or solid effect.
3) Quench surface with running water.
4) Reheat slowly and carefully to remove excess moisture.
5) Let cool and seal with lacquer, followed by 2 coats of Trewax™, drying and buffing after each coat.

Variations: 142a

142a) Kelly green may be obtained by substituting chromium oxide for the dark blue dry pigment. Apply and seal as recommended.

Remarks

This patina is a good example of how pigments (oxides) may be mixed with bismuth nitrate as a binder for coloration. This can be quite handy in the application of multi-patinas.

A very durable indoor patina. Too fragile for most outdoor exposure except in solid form used in multi-patinas.

#143 Rusty Blue Marble

Style Contemporary
Technique Spray and brush
Effect Brown and blue-green marbling over black base coat

Chemical Mixtures

1) Birchwood Casey™ 50/50 mixture
2) Medium cupric nitrate mixture
3) Strong ferric nitrate mixture plus 1/2 teaspoon titanium oxide

or 3a) Strong homemade ferric mixture plus 1/2 teaspoon titanium oxide

Surface Preparation

Sandblasted (180 grit aluminum oxide)

Application

1) Spray cool surface with Birchwood Casey™ 50/50 mixture until entire surface is an even dark, brownish-black. Rinse with running water.
2) Heat surface slowly and evenly until hot. Begin dabbing cupric nitrate mixture onto the surface in a layering fashion. Continue heating and applying until entire surface is covered, similar to Plate #123.
3) Quench surface with running water to help neutralize and set cupric nitrate.
4) Reheat surface until hot and begin dabbing ferric nitrate mixture onto surface. Do not cover all of the blue cupric layer. Allow some to peak through here and there under the brown overlay.
5) Let cool and seal with lacquer, followed by two coats of Trewax™, drying and buffing after each coat.

Variations: 143a, 143b

143a) For a redder overlay, add a few more crystals of ferric nitrate or a few more tablespoons of homemade ferric concentrate to the ferric nitrate titanium oxide mixture.

143b) Eliminating the titanium oxide from the ferric nitrate mixture will result in a transparency to the brown overlay. Greens will begin to appear along with blues in the cupric undercoat. Seal as usual.

Remarks

A very durable patina indoors and somewhat stable outdoors. If dicuprous oxide develops, it may be hard to detect under the ferric overlay.

#144 *Autumn Marble*

Style Contemporary
Technique Brush
Effect Deep, rich brown and ochre marbling

Chemical Mixtures

1) Medium ferric nitrate mixture plus 3 crystals of sodium thiosulfate

or 1a) Strong homemade ferric mixture plus 3 crystals of sodium thiosulfate

2) Weak bismuth nitrate mixture plus:
   a) 1/2 teaspoon titanium oxide
   b) 1/2 teaspoon ferric nitrate crystals (or 1 tablespoon homemade ferric concentrate)

Surface Preparation

Sandblasted

Application

1) Heat surface slowly and evenly until amber coloration begins to appear.
2) Return to lower back or side of piece and begin reheating and applying ferric nitrate-sodium thiosulfate mixture onto surface. Continue until entire surface is covered.
3) Keep heating and begin dabbing bismuth-titanium oxide-ferric nitrate mixture onto brown base coat. Keep heating and applying in a sporadic fashion, stippling as well as laying bristles across the surface, giving circular patterns. Application should result in beige and off-white patterns.
4) Continue heating the surface and dabbing ferric nitrate-sodium thiosulfate onto bismuth underlay, turning the off-white or beige under coat to orange and ochre.
5) Let cool and seal with lacquer, followed by two coats of Trewax™, drying and buffing after each coat.

Variations

None

Remarks

Very durable patina. This patina may be too fragile for outdoor exposure unless well maintained.

#145 Black Marble

Style Contemporary
Technique Spray / Brush
Effect Black marbling with white veins

Chemical Mixtures

1) Birchwood Casey™ 50/50 mixture
2) Medium bismuth nitrate mixture

Surface Preparation

Sandblasted

Application

1) Spray cool surface with Birchwood Casey™ 50/50 mixture until entire piece is a dark brownish-black. Let stand for 30 seconds and rinse with running water.
2) Heat surface until all signs of moisture have disappeared. Keep heating until color change begins to develop.
3) Rub smooth surface with #1 medium steel wool and use a stiff, natural bristle brush on textured areas. A deep steel gray should result.
4) Reheat surface and dab bismuth nitrate mixture onto black base coat by laying bristles on their side. This will bring about a ringing or circular pattern around the bristles. Keep heating and applying in a layering fashion.
5) Quench surface with water. This will not only set but brighten the bismuth nitrate.
6) Slowly reheat to remove all excess moisture.
7) Let cool and seal with lacquer. (Lacquer will darken this patina a great deal; it seems to soak up much of the bismuth patterns). Wax surface with two coats of Trewax™, drying and buffing after each coat.

Variations: 145a

145a) Liver of sulfur may be used instead of Birchwood Casey™ as a base coat. The patina tends to darken a little more with liver than with Birchwood Casey™ when sealed with lacquer.

Remarks

Very durable patina for indoor exposure. Continual maintenance is required for use outdoors.

#146 Green Marble

Style Contemporary / Traditional
Technique Brush / Spray
Effect Green layering over black base coat, resembling green marbling

Chemical Mixtures

1) Birchwood Casey™ 50/50 mixture
2) Medium cupric nitrate mixture

Surface Preparation

Sandblasted

Application

1) Spray cool surface with Birchwood Casey™ mixture until piece has an even dark brownish-black coloration. Thirty (30) seconds after Birchwood Casey™ mixture is sprayed, rinse with running water.
2) Heat surface slowly and evenly until hot or until color change begins to appear.
3) Rub smooth surface with #1 medium steel wool or use a stiff, natural bristle brush on textured areas to remove brown residue.
4) Reheat surface and begin stippling cupric nitrate mixture onto surface. Using a flat brush loaded with cupric, lay and pull the bristles across the surface to create veins. Continue heating and stippling until desired effect is achieved.
5) Quench surface with running water to neutralize and help set the cupric. (Quenching may lighten the finished patina instantly, but the lacquer sealer will darken it again somewhat.)
6) Let cool and seal with lacquer, followed by two coats of Trewax™, drying and buffing after each coat.

Variations: 146a

146a) For a greener marbling effect, add a few crystals of ferric nitrate or a few drops of homemade ferric concentrate to the cupric mixture. Adding more crystals or drops will bring about more of an ochre marbling.

Remarks

Quite durable patina indoors, but unstable out of doors. Never use liver of sulfur as a base coat in this patina as dicuprous oxides will, in time, develop from inside exposure as well. This patina will also tend to darken. This patina works best on smooth surfaces.

#147 Gilt Brown

Style Contemporary
Technique Brush
Effect Glittery gold and iridescent brown. Resembles an old gilded piece when applied in solid fashion.

Chemical Mixtures

1) Medium ferric nitrate mixture plus 3 crystals of sodium thiosulfate

or 1a) Strong homemade ferric nitrate mixture plus 3 crystals of sodium thiosulfate

2) Bronze powder on a dry palette

Surface Preparation

Sand surface to at least a 220 grit finish (320 is preferred)

Application

1) Heat surface until an amber coloration develops.
2) Return to lower back or side of piece and begin dabbing ferric nitrate mixture onto hot surface. Keep heating and dabbing until an even iridescent reddish brown is obtained.
3) Dab loaded ferric nitrate brush onto dry palette containing bronze powder. Pick up quite a bit of bronze powder onto the brush, then apply to the hot surface in a stippling fashion. Keep heating and dabbing until desired effect is achieved.
4) Repeat steps 2 and 3 if necessary.
5) Let piece cool. Be careful not to touch the surface until sealed with lacquer. This patina is quite fragile, and touching the unsealed surface may shift or lift the bronze powder off of the surface. Seal with lacquer, followed by two coats of Trewax™, drying and buffing after each coat.

Variations: 147a, 147b, 147c

147a) For a more solid gilt effect, apply this patina on a sandblasted surface, using 180 grit aluminum oxide.

147b) After the piece is sealed, using Kiwi™ brown shoe wax or a brown Trewax™, or even mixing clear wax with a raw sienna pigment, will give a warmer orange look to the gilt effect.

147c) Aluminum powder may be substituted for bronze powder if more of a silver look is requested.

Remarks

This patina and variations of it are seen more in Asian cultures than in the western world of art. Quite attractive and eye catching, this patina is very durable indoors, but somewhat fragile for outdoor exposure.

#148 *Camouflage*

Style Contemporary
Technique Brush
Effect Beige circular or marbling pattern over dark brown base coat. May resemble lace.

Chemical Mixtures

1) Medium ferric nitrate mixture plus 3 crystals sodium thiosulfate

or 1a) Strong homemade ferric mixture plus 3 crystals sodium thiosulfate

2) Weak bismuth nitrate solution plus:
   a) 1/2 teaspoon titanium oxide
   b) 1/2 teaspoon ferric nitrate or a 1 tablespoon homemade ferric concentrate

Surface Preparation

Sandblasted

Application

1) Heat surface until amber coloration appears.
2) Return to lower back or side of piece and begin reheating and applying ferric nitrate mixture. Keep heating and applying until an even reddish brown coloration is obtained.
3) Continue heating and return to the bottom of the piece. Dab brush into bismuth nitrate mixture and then lay bristles onto surface, depositing a circular pattern, surrounding the bristles. Keep heating and applying in an overlapping fashion until the entire surface is covered. Many layers can result in a nice deep, dusty patina.
4) Let cool and seal with lacquer, followed by two coats of Trewax™, drying and buffing after each coat.

Variations: 148a, 148b

148a) For a greener marbling over the reddish brown base coat, add 1/2 teaspoon chromium oxide to the bismuth nitrate-titanium oxide-ferric nitrate mixture. Apply and seal as recommended.

148b) If a completely opaque light, almost white marbling effect with this patina is requested and it needs to be hot waxed, double the amount of titanium oxide and layer patina several times. The patina prior to hot waxing should be almost white. Waxing will darken this patina considerably, so the patina must be built up in order to compensate for the wax.

Remarks

The more layering of bismuth nitrate mixture, the lighter the patina becomes. An almost completely opaque look may be achieved. This thicker layering also adds great depth and richness not found in many light patinas. Quite durable indoors but a bit fragile for outdoor exposure. Tends to darken at first in sunlight but will lighten in a short period.

#149 *Dakota White Marble*

Style Contemporary
Technique Brush
Effect White and beige marbling

Chemical Mixtures

1) Medium ferric nitrate mixture plus 3 crystals of sodium thiosulfate

or 1a) Strong homemade ferric mixture plus 3 crystals of sodium thiosulfate

White 2) Medium bismuth nitrate mixture plus 1/2 teaspoon titanium oxide

Beige 3) Medium bismuth nitrate mixture plus:
  a) 1/2 teaspoon titanium oxide
  b) 1/2 teaspoon ferric nitrate (or 2 tablespoons homemade ferric concentrate)

Surface Preparation

Sandblasted

Application

1) Heat surface until amber coloration begins to develop.
2) Dab ferric nitrate-sodium thiosulfate mixture onto surface, heating and dabbing until a dark reddish-brown is obtained. Start application from the lower back or side of piece.
3) Return to back or side and begin dabbing bismuth-beige mixture by laying bristles against surface, causing the mixture to be pulled from the bristles onto the hot surface surrounding the brush contact. Keep heating and laying by overlapping the circular patterns, until the entire surface is covered.
4) Return to the lower back or side. Keep heating surface and dab ferric nitrate-sodium thioulfate mixture here and there in an uneven pattern.
5) Return once more to the back or side and begin dabbing white bismuth mixture onto the surface until desired effect is obtained.
6) Repeat steps 3, 4 and 5 if necessary for lighter, deeper effect.
7) Let piece cool and seal with lacquer, followed by two coats of Trewax™, drying and buffing after each coat.

Variations: 149a numerous

149a) Many pigments or oxides may be added to the bismuth mixture for a wide variety of light marbling. This plate was chosen as it seems to be the most popular of this type of bismuth marbling.

Remarks

Quite durable indoors but is somewhat fragile outside, tending to darken at first. As this patina ages out in the elements, it tends to become somewhat blotchy, and eventually takes on a greenish cast, loosing much of its marble pattern.

#150 Pink Marble

Style Contemporary
Technique Brush
Effect A soft pink and white marbling effect

Chemical Mixtures

<u>Pink</u> 1) Medium bismuth nitrate mixture plus:
- a) 1/2 teaspoon titanium oxide
- b) 1/2 teaspoon red ferric oxide
- c) a few crystals ferric nitrate (or a few drops homemade ferric concentrate)

<u>White</u> 2) Medium bismuth nitrate mixture plus 1/2 teaspoon titanium oxide

Surface Preparation

Sandblasted

Application

1) Heat surface until amber coloration begins to appear.
2) Return to lower back or side of piece and begin dabbing pink bismuth mixture in circular as well as stippling patterns. Keep heating and applying until entire surface is covered.
3) Return to lower back or side and begin dabbing white bismuth mixture in circular and stippling patterns over pink under coat. Keep heating and applying until entire surface is covered. Pink under coat should peek through here and there under white marbling.
4) Repeat steps 2 and 3 until the desired effect is achieved.
5) Let cool and seal with lacquer, followed by 2 coats of Trewax™, drying and buffing after each coat. (This patina will darken somewhat when sealed.)

Variations: 150a (numerous)

150a) For a hotter pink marbling, add a little more red ferric oxide to the pink bismuth mixture. If more of a salmon marbling is requested, add a few more crystals of ferric nitrate or a few more drops of homemade ferric concentrate to the pink bismuth mixture.

Remarks

This patina is durable for indoor use but tends to darken with extensive handling. It is too fragile for outdoor exposure, tending to become blotchy and turning green with age.

#151 *Gray Onyx*

Style Contemporary
Technique Brush / Spray
Effect Smoky gray layers over a black base coat

Chemical Mixtures

1) Dilute liver of sulfur mixture
2) Medium bismuth nitrate mixture plus 1/2 teaspoon titanium oxide

Surface Preparation

Sandblasted

Application

1) Spray cool surface with liver of sulfur mixture until entire piece is an even gray black. Rinse with running water.
2) Heat surface slowly and evenly to remove all signs of moisture. Keep heating until hot or until color change begins to appear.
3) Return to lower back or side of piece and begin dabbing bismuth mixture onto black base coat in circular and stipple patterns. Keep heating and applying until entire surface is a whitish gray.
4) Let cool and seal with lacquer, followed by 2 coats of Trewax™, drying and buffing after each coat.

Variations

None

Remarks

Quite durable patina indoors and becomes lighter with age when exposed to outdoor elements. Continuous maintenance is required for this patina if placed outdoors.

#152 Spanish Moss

Style Contemporary
Technique Brush / Spray
Effect Light, opaque, dusty green marbling

Chemical Mixtures

1) Birchwood Casey™ 50/50 mixture
2) Medium cupric nitrate mixture plus:
   a) 1/2 teaspoon bismuth nitrate
   b) a few crystals of ferric nitrate (or a few drops of homemade ferric nitrate concentrate)

Surface Preparation

Sandblasted

Application

1) Spray cool surface with Birchwood Casey™ 50/50 mixture until entire surface is an even brownish black. Let set for 30 seconds, then rinse.
2) Heat surface until all signs of moisture have disappeared. Keep heating until hot.
3) Rub smooth surface with #1 medium steel wool and use a stiff, natural bristle brush on textured areas to remove brown residues, revealing a dark, steel-gray undercoat.
4) Reheat and begin dabbing cupric mixture onto surface in marbling patterns. Keep heating and layering until desired effect is obtained.
5) Quench with running water to help neutralize and set the nitrate mixture.
6) Slowly and carefully reheat surface to remove all signs of moisture.
7) Let cool and seal with lacquer, followed by two coats of Trewax™, drying and buffing after each coat.

Variations: 152a (numerous)

152a) Oxides may be added to the nitrate solution to give varying degrees of coloration. When mixed in the nitrate solution, oxides may tend to cloud this patina, making it even more opaque and blocking much depth.

#153 Roman Brown

Style Contemporary
Technique Brush / Spray
Effect Deep, rich, opaque brown, orange, and ochre patterns over a black base coat

Chemical Mixtures

1) Dilute liver of sulfur mixture
or 1a) Birchwood Casey™ 50/50 mixture
2) Medium cupric nitrate mixture
3) Strong ferric nitrate mixture plus
   a) 1/2 teaspoon bismuth nitrate crystals
   b) 1/2 teaspoon titanium oxide
or 3a) Strong homemade ferric mixture plus:
   a) 1/2 teaspoon bismuth nitrate crystals
   b) 1/2 teaspoon titanium oxide
   c) 2 tablespoons. ferric concentrate

Surface Preparation

Sandblasted

Application

1) Spray liver of sulfur or Birchwood Casey™ 50/50 mixture onto cool surface until an even dark gray black or brown black is achieved. Rinse with running water.
2) Heat surface until hot. Then rub smooth surface with #1 medium steel wool, and use a stiff bristle brush on textured areas to remove residues, exposing a dark steel gray.
3) Reheat surface until hot and begin stippling cupric nitrate onto surface. Keep heating and stippling until entire surface has either green stipples or marbling patterns over the black base coat. (Stippling and marble patterns may be minimal.)
4) Quench surface with running water.
5) Reheat surface slowly and evenly until hot and begin applying ferric nitrate mixture over cupric underlay, in a stippling fashion. Keep heating and stippling until entire surface is covered or desired effect is obtained.
6) Let piece cool and seal with lacquer, followed by two coats of Trewax™, drying and buffing after each coat. (Brown shoe wax or brown colored Trewax™ may be used instead of clear Trewax™ if a deeper brown coloration is desired.)

Variations

None

Remarks

Very durable patina for indoor bronzes but may be too fragile for outdoor exposure. This patina will darken from extensive handling.

#154 Red Marble

Style Contemporary
Technique Brush
Effect Opaque red marble with silver veins

Chemical Mixtures

1) Dilute liver of sulfur mixture
2) Medium silver nitrate mixture plus 1 teaspoon red ferric oxide

Surface Preparation

Sand surface to at least a 220 to 320 grit finish.

Application

1) Spray liver of sulfur onto cool surface until an even dark gray black is obtained. Rinse with running water.
2) Heat surface until hot, then rub smooth areas with #1 medium steel wool, and use a stiff bristle brush on textured surfaces to remove dark residues. A dark steel gray should appear.
3) Reheat surface and begin dabbing silver nitrate mixture slowly onto piece. Heat and dab until entire surface is covered or until desired effect is achieved.
4) Let piece cool and seal with lacquer, followed by two coats of Trewax™, drying and buffing after each coat.

Variations

None

Remarks

Very durable patina both indoors and outdoors if well sealed.

#155 Blue Wave

Style Contemporary
Technique Brush / Spray
Effect Blue-green circular patterns over a black base coat

Chemical Mixtures

1) Birchwood Casey™ 50/50 mixture
2) Medium cupric nitrate mixture

Surface Preparation

Sandblasted

Application

1) Spray cool surface with Birchwood Casey™ 50/50 solution until an even, dark brownish-black is obtained. Rinse with running water.
2) Heat surface until hot or until color change becomes apparent.
3) Rub smooth surface with #1 medium steel wool and use a stiff, natural bristle brush on textured areas to remove brown residues, revealing a steel gray base coat.
4) Reheat surface. Dip brush into cupric nitrate mixture and then lay bristles against surface, causing the cupric to be pulled from the bristles, depositing a bluish green ring or circular pattern around the place of bristle contact. Keep heating and applying in an overlapping fashion until desired effect is obtained.
5) Quench surface with running water.
6) Reheat surface slowly until all signs of moisture are gone.
7) Let cool and seal with lacquer, followed by two coats of Trewax™, drying and buffing after each coat.

Variations

None

Remarks

Very durable patina for indoor use. This patina works well for underwater subjects. This patina is not recommended for outdoor exposure as dicuprous oxides may develop.

#156 *Brown Marble*

Style Contemporary
Technique Brush
Effect Green marbling veins over a dark brown marble base coat

Chemical Mixtures

1) Strong ferric nitrate mixture plus 3 crystals of sodium thiosulfate

or 1a) Strong homemade ferric nitrate mixture plus 3 crystals sodium thiosulfate

2) Medium cupric nitrate mixture

Surface Preparation

Sandblasted

Application

1) Heat surface until amber coloration begins to develop.
2) Return to lower back or side of piece and begin heating and dabbing ferric nitrate solution onto surface. Continue until entire surface is covered.
3) Keep heating bronze and begin dabbing cupric nitrate mixture over brown base coat. Place loaded cupric brush against surface and pull across, depositing line or veins of coloration. Keep heating and dabbing until desired effect is achieved.
4) Let surface cool and seal with lacquer, followed by two coats of Trewax™ drying and buffing after each coat.

Variations

None

Remarks

Very durable patina for indoors, but a bit unstable when exposed to the elements.

#157 Mars Red

Style Contemporary
Technique Brush
Effect Iridescent red with gray-black lacy veins

Chemical Mixtures

1) Medium ferric nitrate mixture plus:
   a) 3 crystals of sodium thiosulfate
   b) 3 tablespoons liver of sulfur concentrate

or 1a) Strong homemade ferric mixture plus:
   a) 3 crystals of sodium thiosulfate
   b) 3 tablespoons liver of sulfur concentrate

Surface Preparation

Sand surface to at least a 220 grit finish. Wipe with xylene on a soft rag or paper towel. Rub surface with a #96 Scotch-Brite™ handpad, followed by #1 medium steel wool.

Application

1) Heat surface slowly until amber coloration begins to appear.
2) Keep heating and begin dabbing ferric nitrate-liver of sulfur mixture onto surface. Apply in a layering fashion until desired effect is achieved.
3) Wax hot surface with Johnson's Paste Wax™. Let cool and buff.

Variations

None

Remarks

A somewhat unstable patina indoors or outdoors. The potash can develop white or cloudy patches on the wax surface. Continual maintenance is required with this patina.

#158 *Aqua Marine*

Style Contemporary
Technique Brush / Spray
Effect Blue-green marbling over a highlighted base coat

Chemical Mixtures

1) Birchwood Casey™ 50/50 mixture
2) Medium cupric nitrate mixture

Surface Preparation

Sandblasted

Application

1) Spray Birchwood Casey™ 50/50 mixture onto cool surface until entire piece is an even dark brownish black. Rinse with running water.
2) Rub wet surface with a # 96 Scotch-Brite™ handpad, removing brownish-black residues until bare metal is exposed. Rinse as you go. Then highlight wet surface by rubbing with #1 medium steel wool, removing more black residues left over from highlighting with a Scotch-Brite™ handpad.
3) Heat surface until amber coloration begins to develop on highlighted areas. Keep heating and dab cupric nitrate mixture onto surface. Lay loaded bristles across surface and pull to form lines or veins in the patina. Keep heating and dabbing until entire surface is covered and/or required result is obtained.
4) Quench surface with running water.
5) Reheat slowly and evenly until all signs of moisture are gone.
6) Let cool and seal with lacquer, followed by 2 coats of Trewax™, drying and buffing after each coat.

Variations

None

Remarks

Stable indoor patina but darkens from extensive handling. Very unstable patina when placed out of doors. Dicuprous oxides tend to develop quickly on silicon bronze.

#159 *Italian Marble*

Style Contemporary
Technique Brush and spray
Effect Dark jade to emerald green marbling over black base coat

Chemical Mixtures

1) Birchwood Casey™ 50/50 mixture
2) Medium cupric nitrate mixture plus a few crystals of ferric nitrate (or a few drops of homemade ferric concentrate)
3) Chromium oxide on dry palette
4) Ochre dry pigment (yellow ferric oxide) on dry palette

Surface Preparation

Sandblasted

Application

1) Spray Birchwood Casey™ 50/50 mixture over cool surface until entire piece has an even dark brownish black coloration. Rinse after waiting 30 seconds.
2) Heat surface slowly and evenly until hot or until color change begins to develop.
3) Rub smooth areas with #1 medium steel wool and textured surface with a stiff, natural bristle brush to remove brown residue, exposing a deep steel gray.
4) Reheat surface. Dab loaded cupric brush into chromium oxide on dry palette, picking up a fair amount of oxide. Then dab loaded brush onto the surface. There should be enough chromium oxide on the brush to turn the cupric patterns green. If too much chromium oxide is applied, a matte green cloudy effect will occur. Keep heating and dabbing, stippling and pulling the brush on its edge, across the surface, creating lines or veins.
5) Occasionally, while dabbing brush and layering, use the same loaded cupric brush and dab onto dry palette containing ochre ferric oxide, applying in a pulling fashion here and there to achieve an occasional ochre patch or vein. This will add interest and rich, contrasting depth to the patina.
6) Keep heating and repeat steps 4 and 5 until desired effect is obtained.
7) Quench with running water.
8) Slowly and carefully reheat surface until all sings of moisture are gone.
9) Let cool and seal with lacquer, followed by two coats of Trewax™, drying and buffing after each coat.

Variations

None

Remarks

Quite durable patina for indoor exposure but very unstable when placed outdoors. This patina works much better on a smooth surface.

#160 Brown Lace

Style Contemporary
Technique Brush
Effect White lacy patterns over a brown base coat

Chemical Mixtures

1) Medium ferric nitrate mixture plus 3 crystals of sodium thiosulfate

or 1a) Strong homemade mixture plus 3 crystals sodium thiosulfate

2) Medium bismuth nitrate mixture plus 1/2 teaspoon titanium oxide

Surface Preparation

Sand surface to at least a 220 grit finish (320 grit is preferred). Wipe surface with xylene on a soft rag or paper towel. Then rub surface with a #96 Scotch-Brite™ handpad.

Application

1) Heat surface until amber coloration appears.
2) Begin dabbing ferric nitrate mixture onto hot surface. Keep heating and dabbing until an even brown base coat is obtained.
3) Return to lower back or side of piece and, while heating, begin dabbing bismuth nitrate-titanium oxide mixture onto brown base coat. Apply in a marbling pattern. Lay loaded bristles against hot surface, depositing bismuth mixture in a circular pattern around the bristle point of contact. Keep heating and overlaying this pattern until entire piece is covered. Then, while piece is still hot, throw bismuth mixture from loaded brush over surface. This will give more of a cloudy, lacy effect.
4) Let cool and seal with lacquer, followed by two coats of Trewax™, drying and buffing after each coat.

Variations

None

Remarks

Very durable patina for indoor exposure, but tends to yellow somewhat with aging when exposed to the outdoor elements.

#161 Persian Brown Marble

Style Contemporary
Technique Brush
Effect Green and beige marbling over an iridescent red and gold base coat

Chemical Mixtures

1) Medium ferric nitrate mixture plus 3 crystals of sodium thiosulfate

or 1a) Strong homemade ferric mixture plus 3 crystals of sodium thiosulfate

2) Medium bismuth nitrate mixture plus:
   a) 1/2 teaspoon cupric nitrate
   b) 1/2 teaspoon titanium oxide
   c) 1/4 teaspoon ferric nitrate crystal (or 1 tablespoon homemade ferric concentrate)

Surface Preparation

Sand surface to at least a 220 to 320 grit finish. Wipe surface with xylene on a soft rag. Rub surface with a #96 Scotch-Brite™ handpad, followed by #1 medium steel wool.

Application

1) Heat surface until amber coloration appears. Then begin dabbing ferric nitrate-sodium thiosulfate mixture onto hot surface, heating and dabbing until a rich iridescent red copper tone is achieved.
2) Continue heating and begin dabbing bismuth-ferric-cupric-titanium mixture over iridescent red base coat. Lay the loaded bristles against the surface, causing the bismuth mixture to be pulled from the brush onto the surface, in a circular pattern surrounding the brush. As layering continues, the brown base coat may lift off here and there during the bismuth application which brings about the gold coloration in an otherwise solid red base coat. Keep heating and layering until desired effect is obtained.
3) Let cool and seal with lacquer, followed by 2 coats of Trewax™, drying and buffing after each coat.

Variations

None

Remarks

Great indoor patina but darkens with extensive handling. Too unstable for outdoor exposure. Does best on smooth surfaces.

#162 *Gray Marble*

Style Contemporary
Technique Brush / Spray
Effect Whitish-gray marbling

Chemical Mixtures

1) Dilute liver of sulfur mixture
2) Medium bismuth nitrate mixture plus 1 teaspoon titanium oxide

Surface Preparation

Sandblasted

Application

1) Spray cool surface with liver of sulfur until an even, dark gray coloration is obtained. Rinse with running water.
2) Heat surface slowly and evenly until hot. Then begin applying bismuth mixture in a dabbing fashion. Lay loaded bristles against hot surface, causing the bismuth mixture to be pulled from the brush and deposited in a circular pattern around bristles. Keep heating and overlaying this pattern. The last layer of bismuth should be thrown from the loaded bristles onto the surface in a spattering fashion. This will fog or cloud the final results.
3) Allow to cool and seal with lacquer, followed by two coats of Trewax™, drying and buffing after each coat.

Variations

None

Remarks

Very durable patina indoors, but tends to lighten when placed outdoors. Maintenance program is required for this patina if placed out in the elements.

#163 Blue Nymph

Style Contemporary
Technique Brush
Effect Blue and white marbling over reflective, sanded surface

Chemical Mixtures

1) Medium cupric nitrate mixture plus 1/4 teaspoon titanium oxide
2) Dark blue dry pigment on dry palette
3) Medium bismuth nitrate mixture plus 1/2 teaspoon titanium oxide

Surface Preparation

Sand surface to at least a 320 grit finish.

Application

1) Heat surface until amber coloration begins to appear.
2) Keep heating and begin dabbing a loaded cupric nitrate brush onto a dry palette, picking up small amounts of dry blue pigment, then applying to the hot surface, in a marbling fashion. Keep heating and layering the cupric mixture, letting the bare metal show through here and there.
3) Quench surface with running water.
4) Reheat surface carefully until hot and begin dabbing bismuth nitrate mixture onto surface. Continue heating and layering until entire surface is covered.
5) Let cool and seal with lacquer, followed by 2 coats of Trewax™, drying and buffing after each coat.

Variations

None

Remarks

Somewhat durable patina for indoors but darkens from extensive handling. This patina is too fragile for outdoor exposure. Keep this patina out of bright or direct sunlight.

#164 Gray Granite

Style Contemporary
Technique Spatter gun or squirt bottle
Effect Dark gray to almost white granite

Chemical Mixtures

1) Dilute liver of sulfur mixture
2) Medium bismuth nitrate mixture plus 1/2 teaspoon titanium oxide

NOTE: The #2 mixture should be made 48 hours prior to use, stirring occasionally. Then agitate once more and let set for 5 minutes. Pour off top milky portion of mixture and use in spatter gun or squirt bottle.

Surface Preparation

Sandblasted

Application

1) Spray cool surface with dilute liver of sulfur mixture until entire piece is a dark gray black. Rinse with running water.
2) Heat surface slowly and evenly until hot or a slight color change begins to appear.
3) Using spatter gun, or squirt bottle set to spatter, spray skimmed bismuth nitrate mixture over surface. Keep heating and spattering until desired effect is achieved. (Be careful not to scorch applied bismuth.)
4) Let cool and seal with lacquer, followed by 2 coats of Trewax™, drying and buffing after each coat.

Variations: 164a, 164b

164a) Zinc nitrate may be used instead of bismuth-titanium oxide for white specks. Can give more depth than a bismuth patina. Use 1 teaspoon zinc to 8 oz. of distilled water.

164b) For a more durable patina effect, a very dilute white acrylic artists' paint may be substituted for bismuth. If the piece is destined for outdoor exposure, an acrylic is recommended over bismuth, as the acrylic binder will far outlast bismuth used as a binder for titanium oxide.

Remarks

Quite durable patina indoors but may tend to brown or yellow when exposed to the outdoors.

#165 Transparent Brown Granite

Style Contemporary
Technique Spatter gun and spray bottle
Effect Iridescent brown, gold, and black speckled granite

Chemical Mixtures

1) Strong ferric nitrate mixture
or 1a) Full strength homemade concentrate
2) Medium ferric nitrate mixture plus 1 teaspoon black ferric oxide

NOTE: Allow #2 mixture to soak for 48 hours prior to use. Agitate occasionally.

Surface Preparation

Sand surface to at least a 220 grit finish (320 grit finish is recommended). Wipe surface with xylene on a soft rag. Then rub surface with a #96 Scotch-Brite™ handpad, followed by #1 medium steel wool.

Application

1) Heat surface slowly and evenly until an amber coloration has developed. Piece should be hot.
2) Spatter strong ferric nitrate solution over surface, giving deep red speckles.
3) Keep heating and spatter ferric nitrate-black ferric oxide over surface.
4) Continue heating and spatter one more coat of strong ferric nitrate mixture over surface. (Steps 2 and 3 may need to be repeated for a required effect.)
5) Let cool and seal with lacquer, followed by 2 coats of Trewax™, drying and buffing after each coat.

Variations: 165a

165a) A diluted mars black acrylic may be substituted for the ferric nitrate-black oxide mixture. (The black pigment used in mars black acrylic paint is black ferric oxide.) The only drawback is that if the Mars Black acrylic is not thinned enough, it may leave an unwanted texture on a smooth surface.

Remarks

Durable patina indoors and outdoors, but tends to darken with age. This patina may also be hot waxed but, once again, will darken more quickly than if sealed with lacquer. This patina is recommended for smooth surfaces

#166 Green Granite

Style Contemporary
Technique Spatter gun or spray bottle
Effect Opaque green or blue-green speckled granite over black base coat

Chemical Mixtures

1) Birchwood Casey™ 50/50 mixture
2) Cupric nitrate mixture plus:

Green
- a) a few crystals ferric nitrate (or a few drops of homemade ferric concentrate)
- b) 1 teaspoon chromium oxide

Black 3) Medium ferric nitrate mixture plus 1 teaspoon black ferric oxide

NOTE: Allow both #2 and #3 mixtures to soak for 48 hours, stirring occasionally prior to use.

Surface Preparation

Sandblasted

Application

1) Spray cool surface with Birchwood Casey™ 50/50 mixture until entire surface is an even brownish black. Rinse with running water.
2) Heat surface slowly and evenly until all signs of moisture are gone. Keep heating until hot or color change begins to develop.
3) Rub smooth surface with #1 medium steel wool to remove brown residues, exposing dark gray base coat.
4) Reheat surface until hot, then begin spattering cupric-ferric-chromium mixture over surface.
5) Keep heating and lightly spatter ferric nitrate-black oxide over surface.
6) Continue heating and repeat steps 4 and 5 if necessary.
7) Let cool and seal with lacquer, followed by 2 coats of Trewax™, drying and buffing after each coat. This patina may also be waxed hot

Variations: 166a

166a) For a green granite with more depth, use a weak cupric nitrate mixture with just a few crystals of ferric nitrate or a few drops of homemade ferric concentrate. Spatter mixture over hot black base coat. Do not use either chromium oxide nor black ferric oxide.

Remarks

Durable patina for indoors but watch for dicuprous oxide development if placed outdoors. Recommended for smooth surfaces only.

#167 *Red Granite*

Style Contemporary
Technique Spatter gun or spray bottle
Effect Red, pink, white and black speckle granite

Chemical Mixtures

Black 1) Medium ferric nitrate mixture plus 1 teaspoon black oxide

Red 2) Medium ferric nitrate mixture plus 1/2 teaspoon red oxide

White 3) Medium bismuth nitrate mixture plus 1/2 teaspoon titanium oxide

NOTE: Allow the above mixtures to soak for 48 hours, agitating occasionally prior to use. Agitate bismuth nitrate mixture and let settle 5 minutes, then pour off the milky top portion for use.

Surface Preparation

Sandblasted (optional)

Application

1) Heat surface until amber coloration is apparent.
2) Keep heating and then spatter black ferric mixture over surface.
3) Continue heating, then spatter red ferric. The surface should be black and red speckled (about 50-50).
4) Then, while still heating, spatter white bismuth mixture over red and black under coats.
5) Repeat spattering red mixture.
6) Steps 2, 3, and 4 may need to be repeated until desired effect is obtained. (Do not overload the surface however, as this patina builds up fast.)
7) Let cool and seal with lacquer, followed by 2 coats of Trewax™, drying and buffing after each coat. This patina may also be sealed by waxing the hot surface with Johnson's Paste Wax™. However, hot waxing darkens this patina considerably.

Variations: 167a

167a) For a pink granite, add 1/2 teaspoon of titanium oxide to the red ferric mixture and use 1/4 teaspoon red ferric oxide instead of 1 teaspoon. Apply the same.

Remarks

Excellent durability indoors and out. Must be well sealed for outdoor exposure. Three to five coats of lacquer are recommended.

#168 *Rocky Mountain Granite*

Style Contemporary
Technique Spatter gun or spray bottle
Effect Beige or buff to brown speckled granite

Chemical Mixtures

1) Dilute liver of sulfur mixture

Black 2) Medium ferric nitrate mixture plus 1 teaspoon black ferric oxide

White 3) Medium bismuth nitrate mixture plus 1/2 teaspoon titanium oxide

4) Strong ferric nitrate mixture

or 4a) Strong homemade ferric mixture

Surface Preparation

Sandblasted

Application

1) Spray dilute liver of sulfur onto cool surface until an even, dark gray black is obtained. Rinse.
2) Heat surface slowly and evenly until hot, then spatter white bismuth mixture over piece until predominantly white, with black specks peeking through.
3) Continue heating and spatter ferric nitrate mixture over white mixture, creating some darker specks. The overall appearance should be more beige.
4) Repeat steps 2 and 3 if necessary, and introducing black spattering here and there to keep interest in the patina (optional).
5) Let cool and seal with lacquer, followed by 2 coats of Trewax™, drying and buffing after each coat.

Variations: 168a

168a) If a browner effect is desired, simply spatter on more strong ferric nitrate mixture.

Remarks

Very durable patina for indoor use, but must be well sealed for outdoor exposure. Tends to darken from extensive handling.

#169 Blue Granite

Style Contemporary
Technique Spatter gun or spray bottle
Effect Various shades of blue speckled granite

Chemical Mixtures

1) Birchwood Casey™ 50/50 mixture
2) Weak cupric nitrate mixture plus 1 teaspoon dry blue pigment (Allow mixture to soak for 48 hours prior to use)

or 2a) A blue acrylic mixture with the consistency of water

Surface Preparation

Sandblasted

Application

1) Spray cool surface with Birchwood Casey™ 50/50 mixture until entire surface is brownish-black. Rinse with running water.
2) Heat surface slowly and evenly until hot, then rub smooth surface with #1 medium steel wool to remove brown residue, exposing steel-gray base coat.
3) Continue heating until hot. Then spatter blue cupric mixture over surface until desired effect is obtained.
4) Let cool and seal with lacquer, followed by 2 coats of Trewax™, drying and buffing after each coat.

Variations: 169a, 169b

169a) For more of a sky blue effect, use a medium strength cupric and do not use any pigment. Proceed with the same application.

169b) If a bluer effect is required, either a blue dye may be added to the lacquer, or a blue leather dye may be sprayed over the hot patina prior to cooling and sealing.

Remarks

Very durable indoor patina but too fragile for outdoor exposure, especially if dyes are used, as most blue dyes are synthetic and tend to fade in sunlight. If piece is destined for the outdoors, a blue acrylic is highly recommended as it will outlast any cupric patina.

#170 *Silver Granite*

Style	Contemporary
Technique	Spatter gun or spray bottle
Effect	Black specks over a silver base coat

Chemical Mixtures

1) Medium silver nitrate mixture
2) Weak ferric nitrate mixture plus 1 teaspoon black ferric oxide

Surface Preparation

Sand surface to at least 320 grit finish. Wipe with xylene. Then rub surface with a #96 Scotch-Brite™ handpad, followed by #1 medium steel wool or rottenstone on a soft rag. Blow clean.

Application

1) Heat surface until amber coloration develops. Keep heating and using a brush, begin dabbing silver nitrate mixture onto surface until nitrate deposit buildup becomes creamy white.
2) Rub surface with "0" steel wool to remove white residues and expose a bright silver base coat.
3) Reheat surface and spatter black ferric nitrate mixture over silver base coat until desired effect is obtained.
4) Cool and seal with lacquer, followed by 2 coats of Trewax™, drying and buffing after each coat.

Variations: 170a

170a) A dilute ammonium sulfide or liver of sulfur mixture may be substituted for the oxide black ferric mixture, but beware that sulfides keep reacting if not neutralized. A wet sponge may help in this procedure. Touch the sponge, loaded with water, against the hot surface to help neutralize sulfides. Do not let water run down surface as this may cause streaking on the silver base coat.

Remarks

Very durable patina indoors or out, but may tend to darken and the silver may loose its luster with age. Recommended for smooth surfaces only.

#171 Ancient Green

Style Classical
Technique Brush or Spray
Effect Mottled blue, green, brown and black

Chemical Mixtures

1) Dilute liver of sulfur mixture
2) Medium cupric nitrate mixture

Surface Preparation

Sandblasted

Application

1) Spray cool surface with liver of sulfur mixture until even, dark gray black. Rinse with running water.
2) Heat surface until hot and dab cupric nitrate onto surface here and there, scorching occasionally.
3) Continue heating and dab dilute liver of sulfur mixture here and there over the cupric, leaving some areas blue.
4) Quench with running water to neutralize cupric and liver mixture.
5) Reheat and repeat steps 2 and 3 if necessary and remember to quench surface afterward.
6) Let cool and wax with clear Trewax™ (optional).

Remarks

There are too many variations with this basic classical look. The idea is to make the surface as old looking as possible. This patina is not recommended for outdoor exposure, but works well for indoor use. Will darken from handling.

#172 *Chiang Green*

Style Classical
Technique Brush or Spray
Effect Blotchy, crusty, green patina, resembling pieces of the bronze age

Chemical Mixtures

1) Dilute liver of sulfur mixture
2) Medium cupric nitrate mixture plus a few crystals or drops of ferric nitrate
3) Patching plaster, modeling paste, or other medium that will give texture to the surface (gesso may also be used)
4) Chromium oxide on a dry palette
5) Rottenstone on a rag or brush

NOTE: The crusty effect for this patina must be accomplished by artificial means, as many chemicals usually incorporated for this look on other alloys will not work well on silicon bronze.

Surface Preparation

Sandblasted

Application

1) Spray cool surface with diluted liver of sulfur until entire piece is a dark gray black. Rinse with water and, using #1 medium steel wool, highlight black from surface, leaving residues here and there. Rinse as you go.
2) Heat surface until hot. Then, using wet brush, stipple either patching plaster, modeling paste, or other material onto surface here and there to give the appearance of a crusty look. Plaster of paris mixed into gesso also works well in achieving this effect.
3) Continue heating and begin dabbing cupric-ferric nitrate mixture over entire surface, heating and dabbing until a somewhat opaque effect is achieved.
4) Wax hot surface with Johnson's Paste Wax™. While piece is still hot, gently wipe most of the wax from the surface with a soft clean rag. This hot wax treatment will bring about a green transparency to the patina.
5) As the piece is cooling, but still warm, place rottenstone on the patinaed surface with a brush and gently wipe excess from piece.
6) Let cool and gently buff, if desired, or leave flat.

Remarks

Too many variations to mention, but this patina can be quite fun. This patina is best used on a casting of poor quality since the rougher and more pitted the surface, the better.

CHAPTER ELEVEN 11

Caring For Bronze

There is a basic truth when purchasing bronze. As collectors we buy a particular bronze because it brings happiness into our lives in one form or another. The hidden purpose of buying a bronze is that we are given the privilege of caring for a particular casting or castings during our lifetime. A bronze may be handed down from generation to generation or may be handled time and time again on the open art market. In any case, especially with antiques, a bronze has gone through and/or will go through the lives of many people.

As a result of bronze artwork being transferred from one climate to another, from being maintained only every other generation, being oiled, scrubbed, etc., the aging patina will go through many changes of its own in its lifetime. All we can do as present collectors is to maintain what beauty we may have before us, or choose to ignore maintenance and hopefully enjoy the eventual changes in the patina.

To help maintain coloration and pattern found in the patina, whether new or antique, a waxing program is recommended at least once a year. The following instructions are recommended for indoor bronze surfaces only. Maintenance programs are more extensive for sculpture placed outdoors and is described in detail in Chapter Twelve.

When a bronze casting leaves the foundry, it may be lacquered and waxed or only waxed. Unless the gallery owner is knowledgeable as to the sculptor's or patineur's finishing requests, the buyer usually will not be able to tell. Therefore, the following is recommended for both surfaces that have been lacquered and waxed, and for those that have been waxed only.

Using a soft, clean dry cloth, wipe the surface gently, inspecting it for any signs of change in the patina. A clean dry paint brush to wipe dust from textured areas is quite handy. A damp cloth may be used to wipe debris, due to handling, from the surface. Dry the surface, shining the old wax coat as you dry. Then, using a soft bristle paint brush, apply a very thin coat of carnauba or beeswax based paste wax to the surface. When a patinaed surface is first waxed, the patina may darken, especially on opaque patinas, but as the wax dries, the color almost always returns. As these natural waxes are suspended in turpentine when purchased in paste wax form, the wax will begin to dry very quickly, and buffing with a clean soft cloth should be carried out within two to five minutes after application. Trewax™ brand paste wax is a carnauba wax based product and is readily available and, therefore, highly recommended over Johnson's Paste Wax™ for many patinas. The oil content in Johnson's may permanently darken lighter patinas. Also, Johnson's Paste Wax™ tends to break down quickly, releasing its shine from the surface in a very short time. Using Johnson's Paste Wax™ on darker patinas is fine, as little or no staining will be seen.

Caring for indoor bronzes exposed to higher rates of humidity may need to be waxed two to three times a year. Never use household cleansers or furniture polishes that may have cleaning agents in them. They will tend to soften and pull any existing protective wax off the surface, possibly exposing the bare patina to an unkind atmosphere.

Remember, the patina is the most fragile part of an artistic piece cast in bronze, so a person should take care not to handle the bronze while he or she is wearing sharp rings or watch bands as these easily scratch the bronze surface. Avoid spilling beverages, especially containing alcohol, on bronzes as this can be quite damaging to a patina.

Finally, patinaed bronzes should be boxed or stored for only short periods of time. It is best for the bronze surface if the sculpture is allowed to remain in an environment of moving air, as this usually helps keep the surface dryer, and trapped gases in the metal or patina have a chance to escape without harming the finished product.

Remember, as a collector, you are only one of many that will care for and maintain a bronze on its long journey. Taking care of bronzes now will help preserve their beauty for generations to come.

PHOTOGRAPHER: DAMIAN ANDRUS

Artist: Lincoln Fox
Title: Dreams of Flight (at Albuquerque International Airport)

CHAPTER TWELVE

12

Life-Size and Monumental Patinas

Many aspects must be taken into consideration when not only choosing a patina for monumental work, whether life-size or larger, but also in its application and future maintenance.

Many sculptors request that their monuments always look newly finished, while others prefer the surface patina to age naturally, mellowing with time. Still others prefer an aged or weathered looking patina for their monumental work because as the finished piece ages, little change will be noticed.

Whatever effect is requested by the sculptor, it is usually up to the patineur to decide how to proceed, not only in the patina application, but more importantly in the protection of the bronze from, in some cases, severe elemental exposure.

In the past, most bronzes could be placed in outdoor settings with little concern as to its surface protection. Wax sealants usually sufficed for keeping the patina intact as well as shielding the bronze surface from natural mild corrosives found in the atmosphere. The bronze alloys of yesteryear usually contained less copper, which allowed natural oxidation to occur at a slower rate.

Today, the patineur of silicon bronze is faced with many more problems, for not only does the alloy contain a higher level of copper, our atmosphere also has become more acidic and, therefore, more corrosive due to man-made pollutants. This is much more of a problem in urban areas than in rural settings. However, as a result of wind patterns and rural population expansion, the challenge of bronze protection is becoming more apparent even in the wide open spaces.

The sun's rays also play a major role in the durability and protection of a bronze patina. This has more to do with surface finish and color choice than anything else. Many dark colors will absorb heat faster, causing the molecular structure to expand at a quicker pace, thus shortening the life span of many protective coatings such as Incralac™. This is especially true where black or dark brown patinas are concerned. Also, dark patinas usually show signs of weathering at a faster rate; that is, collecting dirt and dust particles from the atmosphere. Plus rain tends to show signs of streaking, resulting in vertical coloration patterns that may "break up" form and movement of a bronze sculpture. Rain, together with the accumulation of dust particles, also results in the lightening of dark patinas. Therefore, dark patinas are usually not recommended for outdoor exposure unless either continuous maintenance is carried out or the anticipated natural lighter effects are requested.

On the other end of the color chart, white and other ultra light patinas may also create a problem. Although lacquer sealants tend to last longer on lighter patinas, ultra light patinas usually become dirty and stained at a faster rate. There may be a problem involving the maintenance of ultra light opaque patinas as well. Waxing these surfaces may darken the ultra light opague patinas, especially when the sun warms the bronze surface, possibly changing the patina permanently.

Because nature usually darkens light patinas and lightens dark ones, color values from the middle of the light spectrum are usually recommended unless continual maintenance is arranged. Not only do these middle color values give more protection from the elements, they also may be easier to maintain. Thus, colors such as light browns and greens are most popular for durability and easy maintenance.

SURFACE PREPARATION

Surface preparation is a very important aspect of consideration when dealing with patina durability in an outdoor setting. Highly reflective smooth surfaces containing light transparent patinas increase the reflective rate of ultra violet rays, causing lacquer surfaces to break down at a faster rate and/or darken the light patina as well. If a reflective smooth finish is requested, a lighter copper coloration is recommended, especially over a light golden patina, for its durability.

Sandblasted surfaces are usually considered to be the best for patina and sealant longevity. The "toothing" created by sandblasting usually holds the chemical colorations and sealants better than do highly sanded or polished surfaces, although there are drawbacks to sandblasting an outdoor surface as well.

Large grit sand (30 to 50 grit) is never recommended for blasting monuments destined for outdoor exposure. Not only does the "toothing" created by the use of these large grits have the ability to hold too much of the chemical compounds used for coloration, they may also catch and hold many corrosive pollutants deposited on the surface from the atmosphere. This will ultimately result in patina damage, causing color change and eventual sealant break down.

Higher sand grits are usually recommended for blasting outdoor surfaces, as they still create "toothing" on the surface, but not enough to "hold" or trap many surface contaminates over a long period of time.

Large contemporary silicon bronze sculptures are almost always cast in large sections or panels and then assembled by means of welding. The casting of large pieces, in many instances, raises the chances of creating gas pockets, porosity, etc., due to the large surface; that is, the greater the surface area, the greater the chances of casting flaws. Many foundries have strived to overcome this natural occurrence, and some do better than others. Quality art foundries that are able to keep this problem to a minimum can usually ask more for their castings. The process of eliminating casting flaws requires more steps and manpower, thus demanding higher prices.

For outdoor sculpture, the necessity of a quality casting is essential, as such areas of porosity can lead to patina disfigurement later on. Conservationists deal with this enigma on a daily basis.

SELECTING DURABLE PATINAS

Many monuments are usually commissioned by individuals or organizations, and the sculptor, by working with such parties, usually has the knowledge as to the locations and settings in which these outdoor pieces are to be placed. This information is of prime importance to the patineur, as different environments require special treatments, not only in patina application, but also in sealant protection. Dry climates are usually the easiest to work with if no patina change is requested. Moist, damp climates, on the other hand, carry a multitude of considerations when applying and sealing patinas. This is especially true in urban settings, where sulfide pollutants, together with a damp surface, can damage not only the patina, but the bronze itself.

If a sculptor of a particular monument is unsure as to the final destination of his or her work, then steps should be taken as to ensure a durable patina and sealant for extreme environments. In this case, the patina and sealant should hold up well in either damp or dry climates.

Many chemical compounds used in the art of patination for indoor bronze pieces may be too unstable for outdoor use. This is especially true in the case of silicon bronze. Today, the patineur has many alternative pigment binders at his or her disposal that were unknown in the past. Although historically, many different paints and pigmented varnishes or lacquers were used for coloration, they tended to break down relatively quickly due to their fragility. Because of their chemical makeup, they became too brittle with time and as a result of surface expansion and contraction, from heat radiated by the sun, they were inclined to crack and break away, exposing an unprotected metal surface to the atmosphere. Today, with the use of acrylics as pigment binders, the patineur as well as the sculptor has an entirely new avenue of not only color enhancement, but durable protection for bronze as well. Acrylics give and take with the expansion and contraction of metal, and they have a great binding strength that, in many cases, outlasts their chemical compound counterparts. There are few drawbacks to using acrylics, especially when layering in combination with other chemical compound mixtures to achieve a beautiful artificial patina for outdoor exposure. One of the few drawbacks is that marbleizing and circular or ringing patterns may be almost impossible to achieve. Other than that, they are excellent when used as base coats, underlays, or accent colors to transparent or translucent patinas. Their protective abilities are just as great against our corrosive environment. Incralac™ itself is an acrylic, and for this reason it has long been used as a durable sealant for outdoor exposure of non-ferrous metals.

All chemical compounds used in the patina recipes work well for outdoor purposes when applied and sealed on silicon bronze except for one—cupric nitrate. As mentioned earlier, a nice blue or green opaque patina may develop blood red and brown blotchy patches of coloration on the surface of silicon bronze. This is due to the high copper ratio of this alloy. These blotchy red patterns are a result of a reduction process whereby copper salts (cupric nitrate) placed on the surface of copper or high copper alloys develop what is termed dicuprous oxides. Rarely observed on many lower copper bronze alloys, such as 85-5-5-5, it has always been a nuisance in the art of silicon bronze patination. A blue-green acrylic wash mixture is an excellent substitute for cupric nitrate.

If it is essential to the patina that cupric nitrate be used on outdoor silicon bronze surfaces, then certain steps must be taken in order to slow the dicuprous oxide reduction process. It is hard to say if this process is ever fully controlled. Never use liver of sulfur as a base coat for cupric nitrate on outdoor bronzes as this will only speed up the dicuprous oxide development. Instead, use Birchwood Casey™ M20 and then proceed as usual, keeping in mind that Birchwood™ does not completely control the reduction process of cupric nitrate. Other recommended base coats that work much better than Birchwood Casey™ M20 for cupric nitrate for the outdoors is the use of hot applications, such as the following: 1 teaspoon ferric nitrate crystals and 8 to 10 crystals of sodium thiosulfate per 1 cup of water—applying to the surface until a dark brown is obtained; or 1 teaspoon cobalt nitrate per 1 cup of water—applying to the hot surface until an even, dark brownish-black is achieved.

The author has observed many finished patinas involving the use of cupric nitrate on outdoor surfaces. Various base coat treatments and/or layering techniques were incorporated, not to mention numerous neutralizing skills, to ensure the cessation of oxide development. The patina of greatest longevity was a strong mixture of cupric nitrate, with a few crystals of ferric nitrate to help green the mixture, thinly sprayed over a Birchwood Casey™ base coat (heated and gently rubbed to remove residues). Then the bronze surface was quenched with running water and scrubbed, using a soft bristle scrub brush. The piece was then reheated, quenched and scrubbed thoroughly. After the bronze was reheated once more, and while it was cooling, Incralac™ was sprayed over the surface for protection. This patina was performed 15 years ago and after all of this time, it too is now beginning to develop red dicuprous oxide compounds. The result is minimal, however, showing signs mainly at the feet and lower ankles of an 8 foot standing human figure. This bronze is in a somewhat arid climate and is well maintained by cleaning and rewaxing once a year, which helps in the preservation of this as well as all patinaed surfaces.

APPLICATION TECHNIQUES FOR MONUMENTS

The application of patinas for larger bronze surfaces is basically the same as for smaller pieces, except on a much larger scale. Certain tools used for applying patinas on smaller pieces, such as squirt bottles, airbrushes, and handheld torches, may be inadequate for larger areas destined for coloration. These tools can be incorporated in the execution of a patina; however, uneven coloration may result. Therefore, other equipment designed to broadcast mediums over a larger area are recommended. Instead of using squirt bottles to apply diluted liver of sulfur mixtures or a Birchwood Casey™ 50-50 solution for base coats, etc., it is recommended to use large weed or garden sprayers that are composed completely of plastic. On average, they can hold and broadcast 1 to 3 gallons of mixture over a large area very quickly. This is very important when applying liver of sulfur or Birchwood Casey M20™, as speed is essential in covering the surface, allowing as little sulfide and oxide buildup, which may occur on the lower base sections. Covering the surface quickly also minimizes channeling or deep streaking of dark liver deposits, which may be more difficult to remove if highlighting is required. Always begin spraying liver of sulfur or Birchwood™ from the bottom and work upward, until the entire surface is an even dark gray or brownish-black. If large smooth areas are to be highlighted, it may be necessary to rub these darkened surfaces quickly while still wet, prior to rinsing, as this will help eliminate streaking. Then rinse the entire surface and continue highlighting.

Mixtures for diluted liver of sulfur will vary according to the holding capacity of the sprayer tank. An average mixture consists of 1 pint of liver of sulfur concentrate to 1 gallon of water. This diluted mixture may need to be adjusted according to such things as surface size, temperature, and the particular effect required.

Larger brushes used for applying nitrate mixtures are usually required as they are capable of covering more surface quickly. However, one problem that usually accompanies nitrate application is scorching. This is due more to applying chemical mixtures beyond the correctly heated surface. To help in avoiding or minimizing this problem, larger torches are a must. Using such torches with tips ranging from a 3" to 4" diameter will help in the heating of larger surfaces. Torches designed and sold for such purposes as "weed burners" work quite well in the large scale application of patinas. Care should be taken not to overheat surface areas when using a larger torch. Follow the same recipe instructions for smaller pieces, as to color change, etc., when heating a larger surface.

As mentioned earlier, small airbrushes are usually not recommended when a larger surface is to be covered with an even coating of nitrate mixture. Therefore, spray guns designed for the purpose of painting automobile bodies are recommended. Since most spray guns are equipped with metal reservoirs or canisters, it is essential to ensure that such canisters are lined with either a Teflon™ or some other such coating, as nitrate mixtures will attack the interior of the canister, causing chemical contamination. If budget is not a problem, stainless steel spray guns should be considered for applying patinas, as their canisters are not effected by nitrate mixtures. Spraying applications on large surfaces are carried out in the same fashion as those for smaller pieces; the only difference being, as larger surfaces are to be colored, larger areas are heated and sprayed. The patineur will need to step back from time to time in order to view the large piece and ensure even coating.

The hot patina application on monuments is one that should never be rushed, as scorching and/or uneven coloration may result. On smaller pieces, this problem may be blended using pigmented waxes, etc., but this remedy will not work on larger surfaces. Therefore, patience and time are the two most necessary ingredients when applying patinas on life-size and over life-size pieces.

If dusty, light effects are requested within a monumental patina, the patineur may need to overcompensate with the chemical compound mixtures used, such as bismuth nitrate or titanium oxide. This is because thick coats of lacquer sealants required for outdoor bronze protection may soak up delicate creations. If dusty areas are consumed by Incralac™ coatings, brushing white shoe wax on the surface and then immediately wiping the excess off will help achieve similar results.

SEALANTS

Probably the most important application on the bronze surface destined for the outdoors is its sealant or protective coating. Where sealants are used more on indoor sculpture to protect the patina, sealing a bronze destined for the outdoors is done not only to protect the patina, but the bronze itself. Wax has always been a traditional form of sealing bronze. However, because today's outdoor atmosphere is more corrosive and carries a higher sulfide content stemming from manmade pollutants, the initial sealer needs to be more durable. Lacquers, designed as metal protectants, make great sealants. Incralac™ is one such sealer designed expressly for the protection of copper and its alloys. There are many other lacquers available on the open market. Before choosing any one of these lacquers as a protective sealant, it may be advisable to consult with other patineurs who may be familiar with said product. The author advises the use of Incralac™ on all outdoor exposure, and so further application procedures are executed using this product.

When sealing a bronze surface with Incralac™ or any other lacquer designed for metals, it is highly recommended that they be applied by means of spraying, using a spray gun similar to those utilized by auto body shops (the same type suggested for the spraying of nitrates). These spray guns usually have at least two adjustable valves: one for spray pattern (flat or round) and another valve to adjust the medium flow. For spraying lacquers evenly and with control, set the spray pattern to flat, and the flow to low or minimal. Spraying too much, too fast will only result in runs and sags in the lacquer.

Incralac™ must be thinned if it is to be sprayed onto a bronze surface. As Incralac™ is an acrylic and not a traditional lacquer produced using natural tree resins, common lacquer thinner should never be used. This will shorten the life span of the Incralac™, causing a protective breakdown within a year or so. Therefore, xylene is recommended. Thin the lacquer by at least 30% (thinning Incralac™ up to 50% with xylene may be even more effective). Not only does the thinned Incralac™ pass through the spray gun smoothly, it also lays onto the surface more evenly.

It is advisable to spray Incralac™ onto a warm (never hot) surface as opposed to a cold one, as less moisture may be trapped underneath the protective layer of lacquer. Spray the surface with one thin coat as quickly as possible and allow a few minutes to dry. Then apply a second coat, ensuring that there are no thin spots or gaps in the lacquer seal. If gaps or thin spots are left on the surface, moisture can penetrate these areas and eventually lift the lacquer from the surface, causing damage to the patina and exposing unprotected bronze to the atmosphere. Therefore, it is very important to ensure that the bronze surface is covered as evenly as possible.

For monuments destined for arid climates, two to three coats should be sufficient. However, bronzes to be installed in damp environments may need as many as five coats. Since lacquers tend to be somewhat glossy, there are flattening agents available that are suspended in the lacquer which help to eliminate this "plastic" look.

Always spray the bronze surface with lacquers in as clean an environment as possible. Dust particles may become trapped under the Incralac™, causing unwanted texture and eventual discoloration in the patina. Monuments sealed with lacquers should be given sufficient time to cure (overnight if possible), prior to loading and strapping for transport. This gives the lacquer time to set and harden.

Waxing the lacquered surface is always requested as this also helps to cut the glossy shine left by these sealers and protects them from the environment. Two coats of paste wax are recommended for the final finish, allowing time to dry and buff after each coat. Waxing provides one more protective layer, and it also lays a wax foundation for further coats involved in future maintenance.

MAINTENANCE FOR MONUMENTS

There are many discrepancies as to how and even if outdoor bronze surfaces should be maintained. Historically, conservators of bronze sculpture argued that intentionally maintaining bronze was considered blasphemous to the true aesthetics of the metal. Others argued that the streaking created by rainfall, as well as other atmospheric conditions, were disturbing or disruptive to the flow or movement of a piece. Not until later in the twentieth century did this school of conservation ascertain noticeable damage to the unmaintained bronze surface as well as the monumental structures themselves. They agree that these unprotected surfaces, caused by the lack of maintenance, are being attacked by corrosive chemical compounds suspended in our contemporary atmosphere.

"Regardless of its structural complexity, the rate at which the patina will alter with time is determined by a number of factors—especially the acidity of local rain, the amount of abrasion from particulate material and other accumulated material on the surface, and the amount of water that rests on the surface over a long period of time, which is affected by the ambient relative humidity and temperature levels."[8] As a result, high levels of manmade pollutants, such as sulfides, now suspended in our atmosphere, mix with rain water and quickly becomes a mild corrosive in the form of acid rain, eventually eating into the patina and bronze surface itself. Signs of an aging and decaying patina is its development of green patches, especially where water collects on the surface. These green areas are considered to be bright green copper sulfates. Initially, they tend to show more as streaks in urban areas, then filling in and forming a complete green surface coloration. This natural patina takes on yet other colors due to its new compound developments. Black and dark gray patches may become apparent. This is seen more frequently in large urban areas, as the sulfide concentration is much higher. Eventually, the patina takes on a whitish blue-green patina stemming from newly developed copper hydroxides, sulfides, oxides, sulfates, and chlorides. By the time chlorides have developed, merely cleaning the bronze, either with a mild walnut shell blasting and/or hot waxing, will not do much. These damaging chlorides are merely trapped under the wax surface and may continue to work at the bronze surface, only to reappear on the surface at a later time in bright green patches. At this point, it is best to consult with a professional conservator before blasting and complete restoration.

This natural coloration is seen more in humid climates than in arid zones, where bronzes tend to take on a dark brown-black appearance, with traces of blue-green. This is due, of course, to humidity and precipitation levels.

As all patinas age, they usually begin to darken, due to natural oxidation from the initial chemical compounds used in the patina. As this oxidation continues, if sealed properly, this darkening will be decreased, at least for an extended period. If a continuous maintenance program is enforced, then the life of the patina as well as the protection of the bronze surface may be extended even further. Eventually greens will develop which cannot be avoided and which may add to the beauty of an aging patina. This green, however, can be kept to a minimum, if found offensive, by hot waxing the cleaned surface. To maintain dark browns and other dark patinas, a hot wax treatment is recommended, as this gives much deeper protective penetration than does a cold wax finish and, therefore, holds up longer. Cold waxing is almost always chosen when maintaining lighter patinas as this will not darken the patina as much (that is if the right waxes are used: carnauba based waxes, etc.). However, too much of any wax on a bronze surface will darken any patina when warmed by the sun's rays. If this happens on a light patina, it is usually short lived, however, because as waxes age, they become lighter, releasing the patina lying underneath.

Prior to waxing a sealed surface, it must first be cleaned. If the bronze has been sealed with a lacquer, scrubbing the surface with a soft, natural bristle scrub brush using non-ionic detergent will release many of the seen as well as unseen contaminates deposited there. Then allow the bronze surface to dry, and follow either by carefully heating the surface with a torch and applying wax for darker patinas, or waxing the bronze surface in the cool of the evening, when maintaining lighter coloration. Some patineurs prefer to pressure wash the surface after scrubbing in order to thoroughly clean any loose contamination.

Cleaning and rewaxing outdoor sculpture is recommended at least once a year. If maintaining sculptures in a more humid environment, cleaning and rewaxing two to three times a year is recommended, as this will give excellent protection. Seasonal temperatures can play a major role in the maintenance of patinaed surfaces. The best times to clean and rewax a bronze surface is in the spring and fall, especially for lighter patinas, as the bronze surface will cool more quickly during the early evening hours, allowing the easy application of cool waxing. Another benefit to waiting until this time of day is that the surface and surrounding atmosphere will be at its driest, which is important, since as little moisture as possible should be trapped under protective wax layering.

Many waxes can be used as sealers. The best two are natural waxes such as carnauba wax or beeswax suspended in turpentine. Carnauba wax is found in the Trewax™ paste brand. It is quite handy as it is already premixed. For large areas, the patineur may wish to thin a portion even more by the addition of turpentine, as this may cut down on white speckling and make for a thicker or thinner coating, depending on the amount of turpentine used. Please keep in mind, however, that these natural waxes do have body, and applying very thick coatings will only result in brush strokes and other texture that may be seen when polished. If beeswax is preferred, a standard mixture of 4 oz. beeswax to 1 pint of turpentine is recommended. In either case, buffing should commence as soon as the patina returns to its original coloration. Some patinas may automatically darken, taking days or even weeks to lighten.

If hot waxing is requested, Johnson's Paste Wax™ is recommended as it goes on thinner and doesn't tend to "cake up" or produce unwanted wax texture.

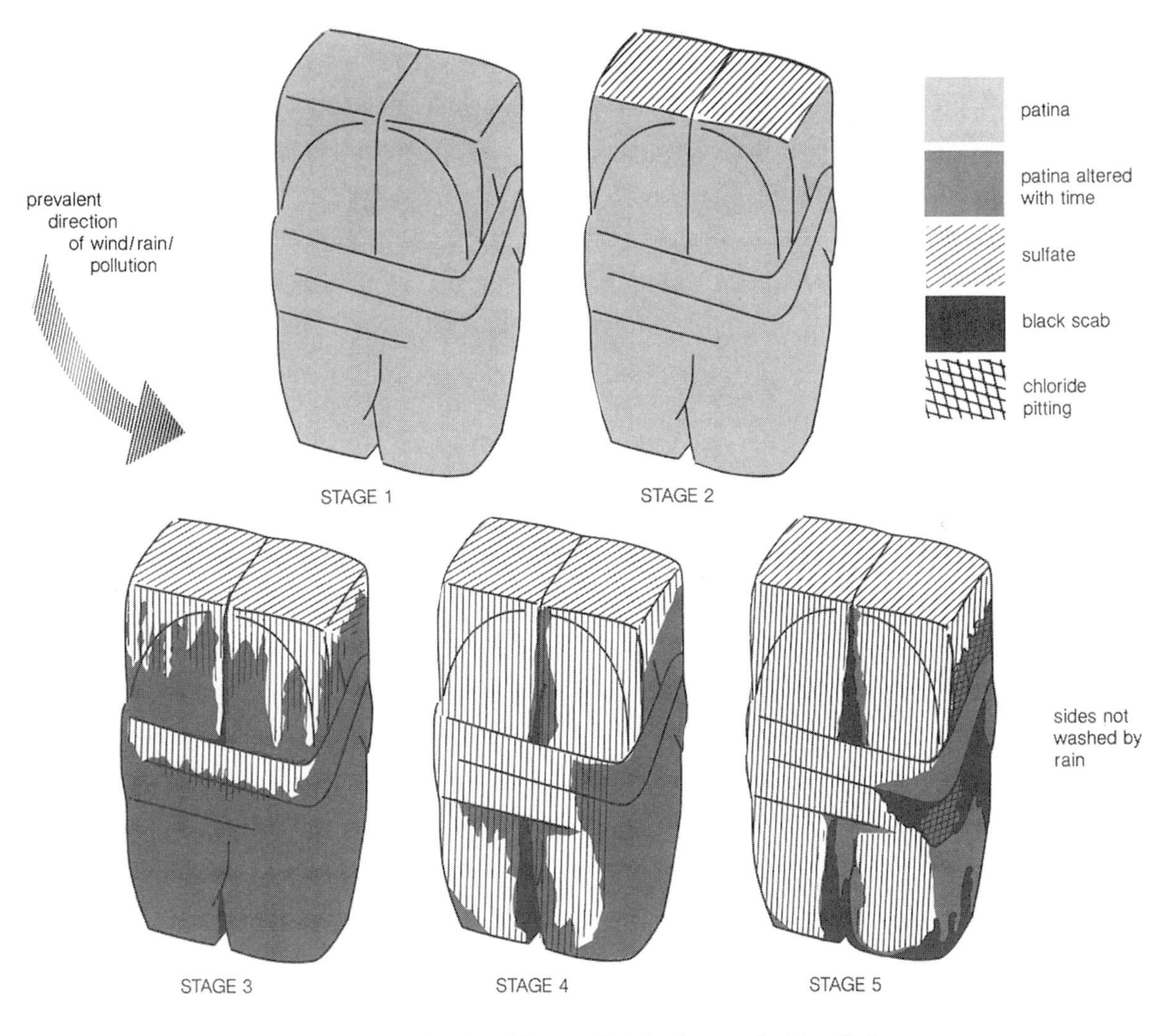

Figure 15: Schematic Drawing of Stages of Deterioration on a Sculptural Surface
(hypothetical bronze casting of Brancusi's *The Kiss*)

Illustration by Mark L. La Riviere, Andrew Lins, "Outdoor Bronzes: Some Basic Metallurgical Considerations", in Sculptural Monuments In an Outdoor Environment, Virgina Naudé, ed., Pennsylvania Academy of the Fine Arts, Philadelphia, 1985

The rule of thumb is that fresh paste wax, because it carries solvents, dissolves other waxes, so whenever applying more than one coat, it is suggested to apply the second coat as carefully and briskly as possible, in order to minimize the disturbance of the primary wax coating.

All waxing of bronze surfaces should be applied using soft bristle brushes. Natural bristles are most proper but are unnecessary for cool waxing, for synthetic bristle brushes work just as well and in many cases are much cheaper. Thin coats of wax should be applied as opposed to thick ones which can also tend to "cake up" or develop wax buildup on the surface, causing possible discoloration.

Allowing wax coatings sufficient time to dry prior to buffing is very important, because if not dry, protective wax coatings could be shifted and/or removed from the bronze surface when rubbing or buffing. Ensure soft, clean, natural fibered cloth used for buffing as these tend to work the best, especially for smooth surfaces. Large nylon bristle brushes may be used for buffing and polishing freshly waxed textured areas.

In many areas of the Southwestern United States, the water is very alkaline, leaving crusty deposits on bronze fountains or other bronze surfaces placed in the paths of sprinkler systems. These deposits may be difficult or even impossible to remove, short of a complete restoration of the bronze patina. If small amounts of these alkaline or calcium deposits are to be removed, a mild solution of vinegar and water may be applied, using a soft scrub brush, and rinsing thoroughly. If higher concentrations are deposited on the surface, then tougher measures may be required, such as using brass wool or a soft Scotch-Brite™ handpad to remove these thicker deposits. There are many commercial cleansers on the market expressly made for removing such deposits from metal. They usually contain phosphoric acid as an active ingredient, and tend to work rather well. Many of these products may be purchased through janitorial supply outlets, or it might be advisable to check with pool supply companies in these areas of the U.S. as they may carry other products associated with the removal of this crusty residue.

Therefore, the patina application, lacquer and wax sealants, as well as a continuous maintenance program are all essential to the lasting beauty of outdoor bronze sculpture. Vast patina changes or shifts are usually a sign of either incorrect patina application, inappropriate lacquer coatings, or more commonly, a lack of cleaning and waxing programs. If the natural look is requested, it is better, in many cases, to choose an artificial patina giving the appearance of a natural one and then sealing and maintaining it, rather than letting the natural reactions occur from the atmosphere onto the surface, as this may be quite damaging to bronze.

All patinas change with time—some easier and faster than others. We as patineurs and art conservators are always learning new aspects about this metal we call bronze. Silicon bronze, relatively new in the world of outdoor monuments, has given us yet another avenue of learning experiences. Using our modern technology, we are making drastic breakthroughs as to possible causes of patina breakdown and ways to avoid these. Hopefully, in the future, we will have new ways of sealing bronze that will last indefinitely. But in the meantime, maintaining the bronze surface is the best bet we have for long lasting artistic beauty and admiration.

Cold Patina Applications

Cold patinas are those whereby various chemical compounds are applied to a cold bronze surface to achieve coloration, as opposed to those previously mentioned that require heat to induce chemical reactions resulting in pigmentation. As mentioned earlier, patinas resulting from cold patina applications are very fragile and unstable on silicon bronze and can be destroyed by the touch of a finger, if not sealed, and therefore should never be used on the professional level. Liver of sulfur and Birchwood Casey™ M20 are the only two chemical compounds used that are an exception to this rule. All other chemical compounds and their mixtures are to be employed strictly for experimentational purposes, because of their unstable and/or damaging reactions to the bronze surface. Experimenting in this field of patinas can be fun and exciting, but as mentioned, the following chemicals are unstable and damaging to bronze, therefore, color and surface change are to be expected over time.

EQUIPMENT AND MATERIALS

All safety requirements acknowledged for the application of hot patina processes are to be followed for cold processes as well, except, of course, for heat and torch safety. The use of rubber gloves and a respirator are especially important as chemical salts used in the cold patina process can become airborne (especially when sprayed) or transferred through the skin's surface, resulting in chemical poisoning.

CHEMICAL COMPOUNDS

Where nitrates are used in the art of hot patina applications, such compounds as chlorides, sulfates, and hydroxides are the major salts incorporated in the art of cold patina processes. Many chemical solutions used in the kitchen for cleaning and cooking are also incorporated in cold patina experimentation, as these help in the achievement of surface coloration.

Below is a list of chemical compounds used, their grade preference, and unique coloration properties. Please refer to Chapter Seven for a full description of such compounds as sulfurated potash, Birchwood Casey™ M20, ferric nitrate, and cupric nitrate. Always refer to the hazards chapter and read all Material Safety Data Sheets pertaining to chemicals, prior to their use. Remember that the individual using these compounds is responsible as to their handling, applications, storage and proper disposal.

These chemical compounds will be suspended in distilled water, usually in various combinations, in order to achieve effective coloration. The mixing and application of these chemical compounds are executed at room temperature.

Chemical Compound	*Grade*	*Color Range*	*Other Reactive Substances*
Ammonium Chloride	tech.	light blue	Urine
Cupric Chloride	tech.	green	Sour milk
Ferric Chloride	tech.	orange or brown	Used kitty litter
Sodium Chloride (table salt)	tech.	reactant	
Ammonium Hydroxide	tech.	reactant blue	
Vinegar (acetic acid)		greens	
Copper Sulfate	tech.	reactant	

Ammonium Chloride NH_4Cl

Ammonium chloride (sal ammoniac) is in a white crystalline form and suspends well in water. It is used in combination with other chemical salts in achieving coloration. By itself, ammonium chloride produces little or no coloration on silicon bronze. This chloride is especially damaging to bronze and copper surfaces, as etching and pitting may occur.

Cupric Chloride $CuCl_2$

Copper chloride is purchased in the form of dark green crystals that suspend well in water. Cupric chloride, just as ammonium chloride, is used in combination with other salts in order to react and deposit coloration on the surface of bronze. Cupric chloride may also be very damaging to the bronze surface as this unstable compound may pit or etch the surface over an extended period of time. Cupric chloride is quite unpredictable when used in patinas exposed to humid atmospheres both indoors and outdoors. When purchasing, do not confuse cupric chloride with cuprous chloride.

Ferric Chloride $FeCl_3$

Ferric trichloride, ferric perchloride, or iron chloride are all synonyms for ferric chloride in solution in order to achieve coloration. Ferric chloride used by itself produces little or no coloration on the surface and, therefore, must be used in combination with other metallic salts when incorporated for patination. Avoid handling these lumps without wearing rubber gloves as this compound may penetrate the skin.

Sodium Chloride $NaCl$

Table salt or rock salt are all sodium chloride. This colorless transparent crystalline compound is one of those chemicals found in the kitchen that, when mixed with other compounds, may react in bright, distinctive colors on bronze. Sodium chloride itself will have little or no effect on the surface of silicon bronze.

Ammonium Hydroxide NH_4OH

Aqua ammonia or household ammonia is manufactured as a cleaning and degreasing agent. It is composed of water and diluted ammonium hydroxide, and will be used in the following recipes instead of pure ammonium hydroxide. The fumes produced by ammonium hydroxide are extremely irritating to the eyes and can be suffocating to the respiratory system. This is another product found in the kitchen which is used for bronze coloration. When ammonium hydroxide is either sprayed or brushed onto the bronze surface, sky blue copper hydroxides are developed, which may be quite fragile if left unprotected. It is used as a bluing agent in some chemical mixtures.

Vinegar (Dilute Acetic Acid)

Vinegar is actually an aqueous solution containing 4% to 8% acetic acid. For the following recipes, vinegar is recommended, and is yet another of those compounds found in the kitchen for cleaning and for the preservation of foods. Vinegar, in time, may turn the surface of bronze to dark green, and when mixed with other compounds, it is used for achieving light blue coloration.

Copper Sulfate $CuSo_4$

Copper sulfate is distinguishable, when purchased, by its deep blue appearance. Usually sold in the form of large crystals, it is quite soluble in water. This metallic salt is used in combination with other compounds in order to obtain patina coloration. Copper sulfate may be used to darken copper but has little effect on bronze unless used in a layering combination using ammonia.

COLD APPLICATION TECHNIQUES

Application techniques for cold patina processes are much more diverse than those used for hot surfaces. Not only are the chemical compounds used for coloration transferred by brush and spray, they may also be wrapped or laid across the surface, producing many interesting patterns. These compounds are also incorporated in "burial or pit" patinas. This type of application involves burying a small bronze in sand, sawdust, kitty litter, etc., that is soaked with chemical contaminants. This moist corrosive atmosphere produces great classical style patinas with only one drawback—their fragility.

Exposing the surface of the bronze to strong oxidizing or corrosive fumes is yet another form of cold patina application. A plastic bag, trash can, barrel, etc., turned upside down over the bronze, will all work sufficiently to create, hold, and keep a mini-corrosive atmosphere when using chemicals that have a high evaporative rate, such as ammonium hydroxide or vinegar. As with hot applications, cold patinas also require a clean surface in order for the compounds to react. Even fingerprints on the surface may have adverse reactions which may inhibit color production. Since cold applications do not bite deep into the surface of the bronze, sandblasting is usually required as this gives a "tooth" to the surface which will hold chemical coloration better than sanded surfaces, which are unable to hold most cold chemical reactions, resulting in flaking and lifting of the patina.

All cold patinas listed must be well sealed if any form of handling or even touching is expected. Waxes will work, but tend to shift and darken a patina. Therefore, Incralac™ or some other metal lacquer is recommended for a first coat. This lacquer coating may be very thin as only enough lacquer is required to keep the wax brush from shifting and lifting the patina.

Two coats of Trewax™ brand paste wax are recommended over the thin coat of lacquer as an outer sealant. Allow each coat time to dry and always buff after each coat. Johnson's Paste Wax™ may be used but will assuredly darken most cold patinas. This darkening may be advantageous in that Johnson's Paste Wax™ applications may give more depth to an otherwise chalky flat appearance. Achieving a more even coloration in a dark patina is yet another reason for using Johnson's.

BRUSH AND SPRAY TECHNIQUES

Use only natural bristle brushes with plastic or non-ferrous ferrules for chemical applications. Plastic squirt bottles are highly recommended for spray applications as they are quite durable and corrosive resistant. Remember always to wear a respirator when spraying chloride mixtures as chlorine gas is produced as a result of chlorides being passed through the atmosphere. All cold patinas, except for liver of sulfur and Birchwood Casey™ M20, need sufficient time to react. Some patinas require only minutes, while others may take days or even weeks. Most cold patinas take time to cure and bite into the surface, once color has been achieved. Rinsing the patinaed surface with running water after the curing period is also a must in helping to neutralize the patina compounds. Then more time must be allotted for the surface to dry thoroughly. A fan works well for the drying process, but it is not advisable to speed up the drying process by heating the surface with an oven or torch as these can easily scorch the finished patina.

Most cold patinas require a damp atmosphere in order for the applied chemicals to react and deposit color. Dry, windy, or breezy environments will dry the chemical solution applied to the surface too quickly, not allowing sufficient time for color production and/or biting. Therefore, tenting a piece when applying cold patinas may be necessary in a more arid climate.

WRAPPING TECHNIQUES

This form of application can be somewhat messy but can be quite rewarding. Strips of cotton cloth are soaked in the chemical solution and then wrapped around or laid across a bronze surface. This not only gives the surface a damp atmosphere, it holds the compounds onto the surface, almost forcing chemical reactions to appear in patterns of one form or another.

Dry wrapping, that is, wrapping dry cotton cloth strips across a surface and then pouring or spraying chemical mixtures here and there, allowing only a few points where the chemicals come in contact with a base coat, can have fantastic effects in a layered patina.

Always ensure plenty of time for a wrapped patina, as once disturbed, it is hard to patch if pulled off too early. Two to three days usually is enough time.

BURIAL OR PIT PATINAS

These applications, whereby a bronze is buried in granular mediums saturated with chemical compounds in order to produce color and pattern, are probably the oldest form of classical style patina reproduction. It is also the most fun. For easy retrieval and containment, purchase a large, dark colored plastic trash can with a tight fitting lid. Depending on the size of bronze, set the piece upright on a brick, or fill the barrel part way with moist contaminated sand, and then lay the piece at an angle. Fill the barrel, packing the contaminated sand gently around the bronze until the entire piece is completely covered. Place the lid over the can or barrel and leave to age for many days. Check the patina progress occasionally by removing sand down to the bronze surface and taking a peek. Such things as urine, sour milk, vinegar, or ammonia may be poured over the mixture from time to time, adding more chemistry to the sand and adding more color to the cold buried patina.

The contaminated sand can be a mixture of a multitude of chemical compounds. Try adding concentrate liver of sulfur, strong cupric nitrate, ammonia, or vinegar, ferric chloride, ammonium chloride, or cupric chloride to the sand, along with enough water to allow the sand to stick together or "ball" up when squeezed. As mentioned, after the bronze is completely covered with this contaminated sand, ammonia can be poured over the top of the mixture for blues, and vinegar can be used more for greens.

Used kitty litter incorporated as a sand substitute works quite well, giving extraordinary results, especially when vinegar, ammonia, or urine is poured over the mixture and allowed to soak down and around the bronze surface.

After the desired effects are achieved, which may take weeks, the buried surface must be thoroughly washed to neutralize any reactions and to remove sand as well as other particulates. Sufficient time should be given for proper drying and curing of a buried patina. Some chemical change may result from exposure to the direct sunlight, so the surface should be dried in the shade, if possible, for at least one week. Then seal it with a thin lacquer coating, followed by one or two coats of Trewax™.

SOME COLD PATINA RECIPES

Apple Green

This application is brushed, sprayed, or wrapped. Must be kept in a moist atmosphere until sufficient time to react.

fi teaspoon	Ammonium Chloride
3 teaspoons	Cupric Chloride
8 oz.	Water

The sandblasted surface is coated evenly with the above solution and must be covered to create a damp environment while reacting. Lift cover and allow time to cure and dry. Rinse thoroughly with running water and allow more drying time, prior to sealing with Incralac™ and wax coatings.

This patina may be transformed into a powdery orange by rinsing the surface thoroughly with hot water as opposed to cold. Interesting orange and red patterns can be obtained across this green chloride patina by placing steel wool here and there on the surface for only a few seconds, while the patina is still wet.

This patina may also be "fumed" by placing a small dish of ammonium hydroxide under the tent containing the wet green bronze surface. These hydroxide fumes will turn the bronze patina more of a blue to powder blue, either all over or just in spots, depending on reaction and drying of the surface.

This apple green chloride patina may be used over a liver of sulfur base coat for a darker, richer patina. The apple green mixture also works well for wrapping techniques. It usually only takes a short time for reaction—two to three days. This patina, as all cold patinas, lightens when dry.

Sky Blue

This recipe comes out of most kitchens worldwide as all of the following chemicals are either used in preparing food, or for cleaning purposes.

8 oz.	White distilled vinegar 4%-8%
1 tablespoon	Sodium chloride (table salt) *Mix the above chemicals in a plastic squirt bottle.*
8 oz.	Household ammonia *Place in a 2nd squirt bottle*

Spray the clean, sandblasted surface containing a liver of sulfur base coat (optional). Keep spraying until the first signs of blue streaking begin to appear. Then stop spraying ammonia and begin to spray the vinegar/salt mixture until the entire surface is well saturated. Allow the surface to dry from a dark grayish-blue (possibly) to an intense powdery sky blue. Rinse thoroughly and seal as requested, when dry.

Peacock Blue

This darker, powdery blue is quite attractive when sprayed over apple green sections of surface, then allowed to dry.

3 teaspoons	Ammonium chloride
fi teaspoon	Cupric chloride
8 oz.	Water

Spray, brush, or wrap surface with the above mixture until signs of blue begin to appear. Quickly place the surface in a humid tent for 5 to 10 minutes and allow it to dry slowly. This patina may be darkened with a liver base coat, and/or using Johnson's Paste Wax™.

Rusty Brown

Opaque brown is quite easy to develop and maintain even though it is a cold patina.

1 tablespoon	Ferric chloride
1 tablespoon	Ferric nitrate crystals
8 oz.	Water

This patina can either be sprayed or brushed onto the surface until well saturated and left to dry. It becomes browner, then lighter as it dries. Rinse thoroughly and allow to cure for one week. Then seal the surface as requested.

Ammonia Blue

The simplest and cheapest of all patinas to obtain is ammonia blue. This is nothing more than spraying ammonia over a dark liver of sulfur base coat, until signs of blue coloration begin to develop. These streaking patterns may become more and more pronounced as spraying continues. When most signs of color development have diminished, leave the surface to dry. Allow one week drying, prior to sealing, or let it go natural. Works well as an outdoor primer for an eventual weathered effect.

Black and Gray

It is proper that the last patina mentioned in cold patina processes is black as this is where the recipes for hot applications begin.

> (See the diluted liver of sulfur mixture found in Chapter 9.)

Spray or brush solution onto surface, concentrating on light areas, until the entire piece is black or dark gray. Rinse thoroughly. For a streaking effect, respray the surface with liver of sulfur after rinsing, and then rinse once again. Allow the surface to dry, then seal with lacquer and /or wax. Johnson's Paste Wax™ will darken this most basic of patinas permanently. This patina can also be lacquered, waxed, or left unsealed in an outdoor setting and allowed to age naturally.

Liver of sulfur, just as all patinas, will come in contact with many adverse conditions causing continuous new and different coloration. It is the pleasure of the owner of the piece to care for and maintain its wax seal, or let it go natural, loosing its sheen with age, followed by the eventual patina breakdown and color transference or change.

CHAPTER FOURTEEN 14

Chemical Hazards

Below is a list of the chemical compounds, their descriptions or physical properties, hazards, emergency first aid associated in reference to each compound, and finally, the incompatibilities. Prior to their handling or use, always refer to the Material Safety Data Sheets (MSDS) that should accompany the sale of most of the following compounds listed.

The following information has been compiled with reference to Material Safety Data Sheets from Mallinckrodt Chemicals and Hawley's Condensed Chemical Dictionary, as well as various chemical suppliers and health organizations. This information is given only as a quick reference to particular chemical compounds. In no way is this information to be a substitute for the full chemical analysis, handling, and safety measurements given in the Material Safety Data Sheets.

The knowledge of the following chemicals listed in their individual MSDS is constantly updated and therefore is subject to change. It is the responsibility of the user of these, or any other chemical compounds, to obtain up-to-date safety information from his or her chemical supplier.

If for any reason any of these chemicals are taken internally, call for medical attention immediately. If the following chemical compounds come in contact with eyes, flush immediately with running water for at least 15 minutes, then seek the closest emergency facility.

Always wear the appropriate protective gear such as eye goggles or safety glasses, a face shield when working with strong acids, a qualified respirator, and good rubber gloves when handling and/or applying the following chemicals.

Keep all of these chemicals in tightly sealed plastic or glass containers and store them in a cool place, OUT OF REACH OF CHILDREN AND PETS.

Any person purchasing and/or using any of the following chemical compounds takes full responsibility for their proper storage, use and disposal.

The following information deals only with the chemical compounds used or mentioned in this book.

AMMONIUM CHLORIDE

Formula NH_4Cl
Description White metal salt in crystalline powder or lumps

Hazards Class: ORM-E

Avoid contact with skin or clothing. Irritates eyes, skin and mucous membranes. Avoid breathing dust. Harmful if swallowed. May be absorbed through the skin.

Emergency First Aid

In case of contact, immediately flush skin or eyes with plenty of water for at least 15 minutes. If swallowed, DO NOT INDUCE VOMITING! Give large quantities of water. Never give anything by mouth to an unconscious person. In all cases, call a physician.

Incompatibilities

Never mix ammonium chloride with concentrated acids, such as nitric, sulfuric, strong bases, silver nitrate, potassium chlorate, ammonium nitrate, bromine triflouride, and iodine heptaflouride.

AMMONIUM HYDROXIDE

Formula NH_4OH
Description Colorless liquid, strong odor

Hazards Class: Corrosive Material

Corrosive in fume and liquid states. May cause severe burns to the skin and eyes. Avoid breathing fumes as they may cause severe damage to all parts of the respiratory system. Keep container closed and use only in a well ventilated area. This substance is classified as a POISON under the Federal Caustic Poison Act.

Emergency First Aid

If swallowed, give several glasses of water to drink to dilute. Vomiting may occur spontaneously, but DO NOT INDUCE! If inhaled, remove person to fresh air. If not breathing, give artificial respiration. If breathing is difficult, give oxygen. In case of contact, immediately flush skin or eyes with plenty of water for at least 15 minutes. In all cases call a physician.

Note: In the recipes in this book, ammonium hydroxide is only used in a very diluted form - household ammonia.

Incompatibilities:

Acids, acrolein, dimethyl sulfate, halogens, SILVER NITRATE

AMMONIUM SULFIDE

Formula $(NH_4)_2S$ in aqueous solution 20-24%

Description Clear, yellow liquid with a strong offensive odor

Hazards Class: Combustible liquid

A strong irritant to the skin and mucous membranes. If taken internally, ammonium sulfide will cause severe damage. In high concentrations, the vapors may cause unconsciousness if inhaled. Ammonium sulfide fumes also may cause head and body aches. Hydrogen sulfide gases are generated when used.

Emergency First Aid

If inhaled, remove person to fresh air. If not breathing, give artificial respiration. If breathing is difficult, give oxygen. If swallowed, induce vomiting immediately by giving two glasses of water and sticking finger down throat. (However, never give anything by mouth to an unconscious person.) In case of contact, immediately flush skin or eyes with plenty of water for at least 15 minutes. In all cases call a physician.

Incompatibilities

Ammonium sulfide should never be mixed with strong acids as explosion will develop, giving off toxic hydrogen sulfide gas. Never mix with oxidizers such as nitrates. Never use on zinc or any zinc compound mentioned in this book.

BIRCHWOOD CASEY™ M20

Formula Mixture

Description Odorless blue liquid

Hazards Class: Corrosive Material

A corrosive liquid that may irritate the eyes and skin. Avoid breathing mist (if sprayed) by wearing a protective respirator. Use in a well-ventilated area. Breathing mists can result in a loss of the sense of smell, in nose and throat irritation, in a garlic odor of breath, headache, dizziness lassitude, tremors, difficulty breathing, bronchitis, pneumonitis and bronchial asthma. If swallowed, it will cause severe internal injury.

Emergency First Aid

If M20 comes in contact with the eyes, rinse thoroughly with running water for at least 15 minutes. Consult a physician immediately. If ingested, INDUCE VOMITING and seek medical attention immediately. If not breathing, provide artificial respiration or oxygen. Wash skin thoroughly if exposed, as redness of the skin may occur. Not normally a skin irritant.

Incompatibilities

Do not mix with organic solvents or reducing agents such as xylene or toluene, oils, or cyanides.

BISMUTH NITRATE

Formula $Bi(No_3)_3\ 5H_2O$
Description Transparent, colorless crystals with a nitric smell

Hazards Class: Oxidizer

Contact with other materials may cause fire. Bismuth is a strong irritant to the eyes, skin and mucous membranes. May be harmful if swallowed, inhaled, or absorbed through the skin. Bismuth nitrate may affect the liver and kidneys. Repeated or prolonged ingestion may cause a "Bismuth line," black spots on the gums, foul breath and salivation.

Emergency First Aid

In case of contact, immediately flush eyes with plenty of water for at least 15 minutes, and seek immediate medical attention. If swallowed, induce vomiting immediately by giving two glasses of water and sticking finger down throat. Also seek medical attention immediately.

Incompatibilities

Paper and other wood products, aluminum, cyanides

CHROMIUM OXIDE

Formula Cr_2O_3
Description: Bright green powder-nuisance particulate

Hazards Class: Metal oxide

Avoid breathing dust as chromium oxide is a suspected carcinogen. Later respiratory problems may develop. May become embedded in the skin, causing bodily contamination. The dust given off may be irritating to the throat and mucous membranes.

Emergency First Aid

If ingested, call physician immediately. If in contact with eyes, rinse eyes for at least 15 minutes and then seek medical attention. Wash thoroughly if in contact with skin.

Incompatibilities

Copper oxide (incandescence), glycerol

CUPRIC CHLORIDE

Formula $CuCl_2$
Description Somewhat clear green crystals

Hazards Class: ORM-E

Avoid breathing dust as cupric chloride is toxic by both inhalation or ingestion. May be irritating to the eyes and mucous membranes. May be absorbed through the skin. Poisoning may affect the liver, kidneys and spleen.

Emergency First Aid

In case of contact, immediately flush skin or eyes with plenty of water for at least 15 minutes. If swallowed, DO NOT INDUCE VOMITING! Give large quantities of water and call a physician immediately.

Incompatibilities

Potassium or sodium as possible explosion may occur upon impact.

CUPRIC NITRATE

Formula $Cu(NO_3)\ 5/2H_2O$
Description Deep blue crystals with a nitric odor

Hazards Class: Oxidizer (strong)

Avoid inhaling or ingesting cupric nitrate. Dust particles may irritate the eyes, skin and mucous membranes. If inhaled, this substance may cause irritation of the upper respiratory tract. Symptoms may include coughing, sore throat and shortness of breath. May also cause symptoms similar to the common cold, including chills and stuffiness of the head. If ingested, cupric nitrate may cause severe internal damage. Central nervous excitation may occur from exposure both from inhaling and ingestion. Persons with pre-existing skin disorders or impaired liver, kidney, and pulmonary function or pre-existing Wilson's disease may be more susceptible to the effects of this material. May cause extreme irritation, redness, pain, discoloration and damage to the skin.

Emergency First Aid

If swallowed, induce vomiting immediately by giving two glasses of water, or milk if available, and sticking finger down throat. Never give anything by mouth to an unconscious person. If inhaled, remove person to fresh air. If not breathing, give artificial respiration. If breathing is difficult, give oxygen. In case of contact, immediately flush skin or eyes with plenty of water for at least 15 minutes. In all cases call a physician.

Incompatibilities

Keep from contact with clothing and other combustible materials such as paper. Avoid contact with potassium ferrocyanide, tin, acetylene, hydrazine, and nitromethane.

CUPRIC SULFATE

Formula $CuSO_4H_2O$

Description Blue crystals, blue crystalline granules, or powder

Hazards Class: ORM-E

Strong irritant to the skin, eyes and mucous membranes. Avoid breathing dust or fumes. Copper sulfate is very toxic, and if taken internally, may cause severe organ damage. If vomiting does not occur immediately, systemic copper poisoning may occur. Symptoms may include capillary damage, headache, cold sweat, weak pulse, kidney and liver damage, central nervous excitation, followed by depression, jaundice, convulsions, paralysis and coma. Death may occur from shock or renal failure. May cause irritation and itching if in contact with skin.

Emergency First Aid

If swallowed, induce vomiting immediately by giving two glasses of water and sticking finger down throat. Never give anything by mouth to an unconscious person. In case of contact, immediately flush skin or eyes with plenty of water for at least 15 minutes. In all cases call a physician immediately.

Incompatibilities

At temperatures greater than 250°C (482°F), the anhydrous salt will ignite hydroxylamine. Solutions are acidic and can react with magnesium to evolve flammable hydrogen gas.

DENATURED ALCOHOL

Formula At least 50 formulations are authorized officially for making denatured alcohol.

Description: Colorless, volatile liquid with ethereal odor

Hazards Class: Flammable liquid (solvent)

Although denatured alcohol is a grain alcohol (ethanol) by law, another liquid is added to it to make it unfit to use as a beverage. These additives make denatured quite toxic if taken internally. May cause severe internal damage and even death. Not normally a skin irritant, denatured alcohol can cause redness and itching due to its additives. The vapors given off by denatured alcohol in high concentrations should not be inhaled. Shortness of breath and dizziness may result.

Emergency First Aid

If in contact, flush eyes with copious amounts of running water for at least 15 minutes and then seek medical attention. If taken internally, call a physician immediately!

Incompatibilities

Denatured alcohol is a flammable liquid and, therefore, should be stored in a cool, dry, flammable-proof cabinet when not in use. Never mix or let come in contact with silver nitrate as it may be quite explosive.

FERRIC CHLORIDE

Formula $FeCl_36H_2O$
Description Yellowish-brown crystals or crystalline lumps

Hazards Class: Not regulated

Ferric chloride, when mixed with water, becomes quite corrosive. If inhaled, fumes from ferric chloride may cause irritation to the respiratory system in the form of coughing, sore throat and labored breathing. If taken internally, it may cause severe damage. May be irritating to the skin and eyes.

Emergency First Aid
If swallowed, induce vomiting immediately by giving two glasses of water and sticking finger down throat. Never give anything by mouth to an unconscious person. If in contact, flush eyes with running water for at least 15 minutes. In all cases, call a physician immediately. If in contact with skin, wash thoroughly with soap and water.

Incompatibilities
Metals, allyl chloride, sodium, potassium. Will react with water to produce toxic and corrosive fumes.

FERRIC NITRATE

Formula $(FeNO_3)\ 9H_2O$
Description Translucent lavender or violet crystals with a nitric odor

Hazards Class: Oxidizer (strong)

Dusts and mists of ferric salts may be irritating to the respiratory tract. Coughing and sneezing may occur. If taken internally, ferric nitrate can cause gastrointestinal irritation, with abdominal cramps, vomiting, diarrhea, and black stool. Pink urine discoloration is a strong indicator of iron poisoning. Liver damage, coma, and death from iron poisoning has been recorded. May cause irritation to the eyes and skin.

Emergency First Aid
If swallowed, induce vomiting immediately by giving two glasses of water and sticking finger down throat. Never give anything by mouth to an unconscious person. If in contact, wash eyes thoroughly with running water for at least 15 minutes. In all cases, call a physician immediately. If inhaled, remove person to fresh air. Get medical attention for any breathing difficulty. If in contact with skin, wash thoroughly with soap and water.

Incompatibilities
Substances may react violently with some organic compounds or reducing agents (organic solvents such as xylene).

FERRIC OXIDE

Formula red Fe_2O_3, black Fe_3O_4
Description Dense red or black powders

Hazards Class: Metal Oxide

Prolonged or repeated contact or acute inhalation may cause skin irritation or pulmonary edema or benign pneumoconiosis. The dusts given off are irritating to the eyes and throat. No known skin irritation is documented. Ferric oxide, as all metal oxides, are considered nuisance particulates and, therefore can be transferred easily by air currents, handling, etc., contaminating clothing, tools, other chemical compound mixtures, and the work place.

Emergency First Aid

If swallowed, seek medical attention immediately. If in contact, wash eyes for at least 15 minutes with running water and then call a physician immediately. If inhaled, remove to fresh air and get immediate medical attention. If in contact with skin, wash thoroughly with soap and water.

Incompatibilities

Reacts violently with strong acids. No other data available.

ISOPROPYL ALCOHOL

Formula $(CH_3)\ CH_2O$
Description Colorless liquid with pleasant odor

Hazards Class: Flammable liquid

Fumes may be irritating to the eyes. Used as an antiseptic on skin. If taken internally, serious gastric disturbances will result. If inhaled, fumes may cause eyes to water and may cause shortness of breath.

Emergency First Aid

If swallowed, call a physician immediately. If inhaled in concentration, remove person to fresh air. If shortness of breath develops and continues, seek immediate medical attention. If in contact, flush eyes with running water for at least 15 minutes and then call a physician.

Incompatibilities

May react with varying degrees of violence when in contact with many oxidants. Quite flammable. Keep away from open flame.

LIVER OF SULFUR

(See Potassium Sulfide)

NITRIC ACID 70%

Formula HNO_3

Description Transparent, colorless or yellowish fuming, suffocating, corrosive liquid

Hazards Class: Oxidizer (quite strong)

A powerful corrosive! Inhalation of vapors can cause breathing difficulties and lead to pneumonia and pulmonary edema, which may be fatal. Vapors may also cause severe irritation of the nose, throat and respiratory tract. If taken internally, severe burns to the mouth, throat, esophagus and gastrointestinal tract will immediately result, followed by internal bleeding, coma and possible death. Can cause redness, pain and severe burns on skin. Concentrated solutions cause deep ulcers and stain skin a yellow or yellow-brown color. Vapors are irritating and may cause damage to eyes. Splashes may cause severe burns and permanent eye damage immediately. Nitric acid is a powerful oxidizer that may cause fires when mixed with organic materials such as paper, sawdust and cotton clothing. This acid is quite reactive with most metals, giving off toxic gasses.

Note: Always keep nitric acid stored in a cool, dark place, preferably in an acid cabinet. Always dilute nitric acid by adding small quantities of acid to water - never vice versa!

Emergency First Aid

If swallowed, DO NOT INDUCE VOMITING! Give large quantities of water or milk if available. Never give anything by mouth to an unconscious person. Call a physician immediately and/or seek the nearest emergency facility at once. If fumes are inhaled, remove person to fresh air. If not breathing, give artificial respiration. If breathing is difficult, give oxygen, and call a physician at once. If in contact with eyes, wash eyes thoroughly with running water for at least 15 minutes, lifting lower and upper eyelids occasionally, then seek immediate medical attention. In case of skin contact, flush area immediately with running water for at least 15 minutes. Remove contaminated clothing at once. If burning of skin persists, seek medical attention, as ulceration may occur.

Incompatibilities

A dangerously powerful oxidizing agent, concentrated nitric acid is incompatible with most substances, especially strong bases, metallic powders, carbides, hydrogen sulfide, turpentine and combustible organics such as paper, wood shavings or sawdust, as well as cotton and wool textiles. Also, quite reactive on metal surfaces.

POTASSIUM DICHROMATE

Formula $K_2Cr_2O_7$

Description Bright, yellowish-red, transparent crystals

Hazards Class: ORM-E

Potassium dichromate is a suspected carcinogen. Avoid direct contact with skin, eyes, and internal contamination. If inhaled, irritation to the respiratory tract, coughing, wheezing, fever, headache and labored breathing may result. Inhaling dust or fumes may produce pulmonary sensitization. If ingested, abdominal pain, vomiting, dizziness, intense thirst, fever, coma and liver damage may occur. Death may result from circulatory collapse or renal failure. (Estimated lethal dose - 5 grams.) If in contact with eyes, potassium dichromate may cause severe irritation, redness, pain and conjunctivitis. If on skin, irritation, ulceration and scarring may occur. Skin may become sensitized. Absorption through the skin may cause systemic poisoning symptoms that parallel ingestion.

Emergency First Aid

If swallowed, induce vomiting immediately by giving two glasses of water and sticking finger down throat. Never give anything by mouth to an unconscious person. Call physician immediately. If inhaled, remove person to fresh air. If not breathing, give artificial respiration. If breathing is difficult, give oxygen. Call a physician immediately. In case of contact, wash eyes thoroughly with running water for at least 15 minutes, then seek medical attention at once. If potassium dichromate comes in contact with skin, wash thoroughly with plenty of soap and water and remove contaminated clothing and shoes. If redness or irritation is noticed, see a physician immediately.

Incompatibilities

Never mix with reducing agents, acetone plus sulfuric acid, hydrazine, and hydroxylamine.

POTASSIUM SULFIDE

Formula K_2S

Description Yellow lumps or chips with distinct pungent odor (resembling rotten eggs)

Hazards Class: Not regulated

Dust from potassium sulfide is corrosive and may irritate the eyes, throat and respiratory system. In sprayed solution, hydrogen sulfide gas is emitted, causing headache, body aches, sore throat and gastrointestinal disorders. If taken internally, nausea, vomiting and diarrhea can occur. Mildly corrosive to mucous membranes due to hydrolysis of potassium sulfide but greater danger is the formation of hydrogen sulfide in the stomach and its absorption. Irritating to the eyes in solution, causing conjunctivitis, photophobia, pain and blurred vision. Mildly irritating to skin, and is used in some therapeutic treatments of certain skin diseases.

Note: Potassium sulfide is flammable in solid form.

Emergency First Aid

If swallowed, induce vomiting immediately by giving two glasses of water, or milk if available, and sticking finger down throat. Call a physician immediately. If inhaled in large concentrations, remove person to fresh air. Get medical attention for any breathing difficulty. If in contact, wash eyes thoroughly for 15 minutes and seek immediate medical attention. If exposed to skin, wash thoroughly with soap and water. If redness or irritation develops, seek medical attention.

Incompatibilities

Never mix with strong oxidizing agents, halogens and halogenated organic compounds.

SILVER NITRATE

Formula $AgNO_3$

Description: Colorless, flat transparent crystals with no odor

Hazards Class: Oxidizer

Irritating to the respiratory tract, if inhaled. May cause sore throat, headache, coughing and shortness of breath. Dust deposits in the lungs may resemble a form of pneumonconiosis. Silver nitrate is considered a poison, and if ingested, symptoms include pain and burning in the mouth, blackening of the skin and mucous membranes, throat, and abdomen, salivation, vomiting of black material, diarrhea, collapse, shock, coma and death. If in contact with the eyes, corrosive effects, pain, irritation and possible eye damage may occur. The skin will stain black from contact with this chemical. Local corrosive effects, including skin irritation and pain, may also occur. Repeated application or ingestion causes a permanent bluish discoloration of the skin, conjunctiva and mucous membranes. Repeated inhalation may cause lung disease.

Emergency First Aid

If inhaled, remove person to fresh air. Get immediate medical attention for any breathing difficulty. If swallowed, do NOT induce vomiting. Give large quantities of water. Never give anything by mouth to an unconscious person. Call a physician immediately. If in contact, wash eyes thoroughly with running water for at least 15 minutes, lifting lower and upper eyelids occasionally. Get medical attention immediately. If in contact with skin, wash with soap and water immediately. If irritation develops or persists, seek medical attention.

Incompatibilities

Ammonia, alkalies, antimony salts, arsenites, bromides, carbonates, chlorides, iodides, thiocyanates, ferrous salts, phosphates, tannic acid and tartrates.

SODIUM CHLORIDE

Formula NaCl
Description White crystalline (table salt)

Hazards Class: Not regulated

No significant hazards. If taken in large quantities, vomiting, diarrhea and prostration may occur. Dehydration and congestion occur in most internal organs. This chemical is mainly an eye irritant, causing burns and possible eye damage.

Emergency First Aid

If in contact, wash eyes thoroughly with running water. Get medical attention if irritation develops. If salt dust is inhaled, remove person to fresh air. Get medical attention for any breathing difficulty.

Incompatibilities

Lithium, bromide trifluoride

SODIUM THIOSULFATE

Formula $Na_2S_2O_35H_2O$
Description Monoclinic, colorless crystals

Hazards Class: Not regulated

Dust may cause irritation to the mucous membranes. Diarrhea may occur by ingestion of large quantities. Irritation may occur from prolonged skin contact. Contact with eyes may cause mechanical irritation. No significant irritation to skin unless with repeated exposure.

Emergency First Aid

If a large quantity of dust particles is inhaled, remove to fresh air. Get medical attention for any breathing difficulty. If ingested, give several glasses of water to drink to dilute. If large amounts were swallowed, get medical attention. If in contact, wash eyes thoroughly with running water. Get medical attention if irritation develops. If in contact with skin, wash thoroughly with soap and water. Seek medical attention if irritation and/or rash develops.

Incompatibilities

Sodium nitrate, halogens and oxidizing agents. Reacts violently with strong acids to produce sulfur dioxide gas.

STANNIC OXIDE (TIN OXIDE)

Formula SnO_2
Description White powder

Hazards Class: Metal oxide

Dust from this chemical may irritate the eyes, nose, throat and mucous membranes. May cause cramping, diarrhea and gastrointestinal complications if swallowed. No significant irritation to skin.

Emergency First Aid

If dust is inhaled, remove person to fresh air. If breathing becomes difficult, seek medical advice immediately. If ingested, call a physician immediately. If in contact, wash eyes thoroughly with running water for at least 15 minutes, then seek medical attention. If in contact with skin, wash with soap and water. If irritation develops or persists, seek medical attention.

Incompatibilities

Reacts violently with chlorine trifluoride, hydrogen trisulphide, magnesium and aluminum powder.

SULFURATED POTASH

(See Potassium Sulfide)

SULFURIC ACID

Formula H_2SO_4
Description Colorless, oily liquid with no odor

Hazards Class: Corrosive material

Inhalation produces damaging effects on the mucous membranes and upper respiratory tract. May cause lung edema. Symptoms may include irritation of the nose and throat, and labored breathing. This acid is quite corrosive and swallowing it can cause severe burns of the mouth, throat and stomach, leading to death. It can also cause sore throat, vomiting and diarrhea. If in contact, splashes can cause blurred vision, redness, pain and severe tissue burns. If in contact with skin, redness, pain and severe burns can occur. Long-term exposure to mist or vapors may cause damage to teeth.

Emergency First Aid

If fumes are inhaled, remove person to fresh air. If not breathing, give artificial respiration. If breathing is difficult, give oxygen. Call physician. If swallowed, do NOT induce vomiting. Give large quantities of water or milk if available. Call a physician immediately. Never give anything by mouth to an unconscious person. If in contact, wash eyes with running water for at least 15 minutes, lifting lower and upper eyelids occasionally. Get medical attention immediately. If in contact with skin, immediately wash with plenty of water for at least 15 minutes, while removing contaminated clothing and shoes. Call a physician immediately.

Incompatibilities

Water, bases, organic material, halogens, metal acetylides, oxides and hydrides, strong oxidizing and reducing agents and many other reactive substances.

TITANIUM OXIDE

Formula: TiO_2
Description White powder

Hazards Class: Metal oxide

No significant hazards. If dust is inhaled, the nose, mucous membranes and throat may become irritated. If large quantities are ingested, cramping and diarrhea may occur. Irritating to the eyes and therefore may cause redness and burning. No significant hazards to the skin.

Emergency First Aid

If in contact, wash eyes thoroughly with running water for 15 minutes. If redness or any other sign develops or persists, seek medical attention. If ingested, rinse mouth with water and give plenty of water to drink, then call a physician immediately. If inhaled, remove person to fresh air, and then seek medical attention if any breathing difficulty develops. Wash skin with soap and water after use. If any irritation on the skin develops, seek medical advice. Not normally a skin irritant.

Incompatibilities

None known

TOLUENE

Formula $C_6H_5CH_3$
Description Colorless liquid with a benzene-like odor

Hazards Class: Organic solvent, reducer

This solvent is considered a suspected carcinogen. Vapors are quite harmful to the upper respiratory system, causing irritation to the eyes, throat, nose and skin. Headaches, dizziness and difficulty breathing may all occur from the strong fumes. Reports have associated repeated overexposure with solvents to permanent brain and nervous system damage. Concentrated fumes may be fatal. If ingested, severe internal damage will occur. May be blinding if in contact with eyes. May be absorbed through the skin.

Note: Flammable: Dangerous fire risk. Fumes may be explosive. Store in a fire-proof cabinet.

Emergency First Aid

If swallowed, do NOT induce vomiting. Call a physician immediately. If in contact, wash eyes thoroughly with running water for at least 15 minutes, then seek immediate medical attention. For skin contact, wash thoroughly and if irritation develops, seek medical advice. If overcome by vapors, remove person to fresh air. If not breathing, give artificial respiration. If breathing is difficult, give oxygen. In all cases, call a physician immediately.

Incompatibilities

Potassium sulfide, sulfuric acid, potassium dichromate, nitric acid, ferric nitrate, silver nitrate, cupric nitrate, bismuth nitrate, Birchwood Casey™ M20, Ammonium sulfide and ammonia.

TURPENTINE

Formula: $C_{10}H_{16}$
Description: Colorless liquid with a penetrating odor

Hazards: Class: Organic Solvent

Avoid breathing fumes, as they may irritate the eyes, nose, throat and mucous membranes. High concentration of fumes may be harmful or fatal. If swallowed, severe internal injury and death may result. Avoid contact with eyes, as tissue damage may occur. If in contact with skin, redness and mild irritation may occur. Work in a ventilated area.

Note: Flammable liquid and combustible fumes in high concentrations. Storage in a flame-proof cabinet is recommended.

Emergency First Aid

If swallowed, do NOT induce vomiting. Give one to two glasses of water or milk, and call a physician immediately. In case of eye contact, wash eyes with running water for at least 15 minutes and seek immediate medical attention. If overcome by vapors, remove person to fresh air. If breathing is difficult, give oxygen. If breathing has stopped, give artificial respiration. In all cases, call a physician. For skin contact, wash thoroughly with soap and water. If irritation develops, seek medical advice.

Incompatibilities

Potassium sulfide, sulfuric acid, potassium dichromate, nitric acid, ferric nitrate, silver nitrate, Birchwood Casey™ M20, Ammonium Sulfide and ammonia.

VINEGAR (acetic acid 4 to 8%)

Formula CH_3COOH
Description Brown or colorless liquid with strong pungent odor

Hazards Class: Not regulated

No significant hazards. Fumes may be irritating to eyes, nose, throat and mucous membranes. If in eyes, redness, burning, and damage may result.

Emergency First Aid

If in contact, flush eyes thoroughly for 15 minutes with running water, and call a physician immediately. If overcome by fumes, remove person to fresh air. Wash hands and skin thoroughly with soap and water after use.

Incompatibilities

Strong bases

XYLENE (XYLOL)

Formula $C_6H_4(CH_3)_2$

Description Colorless liquid with an aromatic hydrocarbon odor

Hazards Class: Organic Solvent, reducer

Vapor is quite harmful. May affect the brain or nervous system causing dizziness, headache, and nausea. A suspected carcinogen. Fumes may be irritating to the eyes, nose, throat and skin. Systemic poisoning may occur from contact with skin. If splashed in eyes, severe redness, blurred vision, severe pain and tissue damage may result. If swallowed, severe internal damage and death may result.

Note: Extremely flammable, and fumes are very explosive in concentrated form. Good ventilation is a must when working with this compound. All flames or sources of static electricity must be eliminated prior to use. Storage in a flame-proof cabinet is recommended.

Emergency First Aid

If swallowed, do NOT induce vomiting. Call a physician immediately. In case of eye contact, wash thoroughly with running water for at least 15 minutes, lifting the lower and upper eyelids occasionally, then seek immediate medical attention. If overcome by vapors, or if headache or dizziness develops, remove person to fresh air. If breathing is difficult, give oxygen. If breathing has stopped, give artificial respiration. Get immediate medical attention for any breathing disorder. If in contact with skin, wash thoroughly with soap and water. If redness or any sign of irritation develops, seek medical attention.

Incompatibilities

Potassium sulfide, sulfuric acid, potassium dichromate, nitric acid, ferric nitrate, silver nitrate, cupric nitrate, bismuth nitrate, Birchwood Casey™ M20, ammonium sulfide and ammonia.

ZINC NITRATE

Formula $Zn(NO_3)_2xH_2O$
Description Colorless or white crystals or flakes with a slight nitric odor

Hazards Class: Oxidizer

Zinc nitrate is a corrosive. If appreciable amounts are ingested, abdominal pain, cramps and nausea may result together with faintness and bluish lips and skin. Severe internal damage may result. This compound is quite irritating to the respiratory tract, causing coughing, labored breathing and possibly a sore throat. If in contact, eyes may become irritated, resulting in blurred vision and possible tissue damage. If in contact with skin, redness, pain and possible burning may occur.

Emergency First Aid

If inhaled, remove person to fresh air. If not breathing, give artificial respiration. If breathing is difficult, give oxygen. In all cases of respiratory trouble, seek medical attention. If swallowed, do NOT induce vomiting. Give large quantities of water or milk if available. Call a physician immediately. Never give anything by mouth to an unconscious person. If in contact, wash eyes thoroughly with running water for at least 15 minutes, then seek immediate medical attention. If in contact with skin, wash thoroughly with soap and water. If redness or any other form of epidermal irritation occurs, seek medical attention.

Incompatibilities

Metal powders, cyanides, sodium hypophosphite. stannic chloride, phosphorus, thiocyanates, organic materials. Substance is capable of reacting rapidly with reducing agents and combustible materials at elevated temperatures.

Glossary of Terms

Alchemy
Chemistry in European cultures during the middle ages. One of the goals of alchemy was to turn baser metals into gold.

Alkali
Any base or hydroxide that can neutralize acids. Any base mixtures with pH levels above 7. A soil mixture containing a mineral salt or salts is considered alkaline.

Alloy
A metal that is a mixture of two or more different metals, and/or by the addition of various other substances.

Artificial Patinas
Chemical compounds intentionally placed on the surface of bronze to induce coloration.

Bead Blasting
Using compressed air to bombard glass beads against the surface of metal in order to clean and/or shine the metal.

Brass
Any alloy consisting primarily of copper and zinc.

Bronze
Traditionally, any alloy consisting primarily of copper and tin. Modern alloys have replaced tin with cheaper minerals and/or non-metallic elements.

Bronze Age
Period in civilization from roughly 3000 B.C.E. to 1000 B.C.E.. This period is so named because bronze was developed and became the metal of choice for tools and weaponry.

Buried Patinas
A type of application whereby bronze is buried in sands and other such mediums containing chemical compounds to induce coloration. Surface coloration and patterns from buried patinas are to resemble natural patinas.

Burnished
To make a bare metal surface become shiny by rubbing.

Carcinogen
Any substance that has the ability to cause or help in the development of cancer in humans and animals.

Chasing
Foundry term used to describe the moving of the surface. To remove flaws from the surface of a poured wax or metal casting. To remove welds.

Classical Patina
A style of artificial patina which is to resemble a natural patina as closely as possible. Greens, blues, blacks, and some reds, are the usual colors developed.

Cold Application
Applying chemical mixtures to a cool metal surface, usually at room temperature, to obtain patina coloration. Usually very fragile patinas—not very durable as a rule.

Contamination
Any foreign substance, oxides, etc., on the bronze surface that may interfere with patina application, color adherence and durability.

Contemporary Patinas
A style of patina which goes beyond traditional patinas. Avante Garde school of patination where marble, granite and other patterns are used. Usually more vibrant and colorful than traditional patinas.

Copper
A reddish element that is resistant to corrosion. The primary metal used in bronze alloys.

Copper Age
Period of civilization that dates after the stone age and precedes the bronze age. This period of history is recognized by the building of the pyramids of Giza in Egypt.

Corrosion
An eating away at the surface of metals caused by oxidation. Usually strong acids are involved.

Dicuprous Oxides
Copper oxides brought about by the reduction of copper salts placed on copper or high copper alloys. Red blotches that appear on cupric nitrate patinas placed on silicon bronze.

Everdur
A group of alloys with a high copper ratio, containing the element of silicon. Type "A" bronze. Most common alloy used for casting bronze sculpture in the Americas is 95% copper, 4% silicon, and 1% manganese, with occasional traces of iron.

Ferrous
Derived from the latin word for iron. Used to describe chemical salts containing iron.

Gilding
To resemble gold by painting, or applying thin layers of gold leaf or powder.

Glass Bead
A medium used in blasting the surface of metal for cleaning and finishing purposes.

Gold Leaf
A thin hammered sheet of gold that may be somewhat translucent. Used in gilding to cover metal, wood, and stone surfaces.

Grit
In reference to sand, the fineness or coarseness of its grain. A measurement of grain size.

Heat Scale
A burned or scorched area on the surface of metal, usually indicated by bright blue, violet, purple, and red coloration in a circular pattern. Another term for a welding scorch. In patinas it refers to overheating the surface, causing the development of the above mentioned colors.

Hot Application
Applying chemical mixtures to a hot metal surface in order to obtain patina coloration. Most durable application of patinas.

Hue
Color. A modification of basic colors.

Inorganic
In chemistry, compounds that do not contain carbon and are derived from mineral sources. Not having the organized structure of living things.

Iron
Ferrous. A metallic chemical element that is gray in coloration, and turns red, orange and brown as a result of oxidation or rusting. In patinas, used in a nitrate compound to obtain coloration of yellow, orange, brown, and burgundy. Used in oxide salts for yellow, red, orange, and black pigments.

Iron Age
A period of civilization around 1000 B.C.E. to 100 A.D. categorized by the use of iron, replacing bronze as the major metal of choice for the manufacturing of tools and weaponry.

Master Patineur
Traditionally, an individual with at least seven years of continuous experience in the art of patination. Any person who has mastered the control of coloration from chemical reactions on bronze sculpture.

Marbleizing
To make to resemble patterns found in marble.

Metallic
Having high reflective qualities of burnished metal. To look like metal.

Natural Patina
The eventual coloration of bronze due to the extended exposure to its natural surroundings. Greens, blues, and blacks are typical natural colors for bronze and copper.

Non-ferrous
Any metal alloy without the presence of iron.

Oxidizing
A reduction process whereby oxides are deposited on the surface of metal, causing color change, which may inhibit patination.

Patina
Traditionally, the coloration on the surface of metals and woods brought about by the extended exposure to their surroundings. Today, it is termed more for the coloration on the surface of bronze achieved by artificial or natural means.

Patineur
An individual who applies patinas artistically.

Pickling
A type of metal surface cleaning and etching by the use of dilute acid washes.

Polish
In metal finishing, to bring to a mirror-like reflective finish. To shine.

Porosity
In metals, the quality of being porous or having many pores (small holes) in or on the surface.

Salts
A compound consisting of two or more elements. A chemical compound derived from an acid by replacing hydrogen, wholly or partly, with a metal or an electropositive radical.

Sandblasting
A form of metal surface cleaning using compressed air to bombard grains of sand against the surface.

Sanding
In metal finishing, to smooth the surface using various fine natural or synthetic grits, bonded to or enmeshed in paper, cloth or mesh.

Silicon Bronze
Presently, the copper alloy used primarily in the Americas for casting sculpture. Its alloy make-up is 95% copper, 4% silicon, and 1% manganese. The family of bronze alloys containing silicon as the second major element.

Stone Age
The first civilization of man characterized by the use of stone for tools and weaponry.

Tensile Strength
The measurement of resistance to lengthwise stress, rated just before tearing apart.

Toothing
Sharp microscopic indentations in the surface of metal produced by sand blasting.

Traditional Patinas
Patinas of the seventeenth through the nineteenth centuries. More subdued colors used to resemble antique or older bronzes. What most people think of when they speak of bronze.

Value
The lightness or darkness of a color or hue.

List of Chemical Compounds

Ammonium Chloride

Ammonium Hydroxide (Ammonia)

Ammonium Sulfide

Birchwood Casey™ M20

Bismuth Nitrate

Chromium Oxide

Copper sulfate

Cupric Chloride

Cupric Nitrate

Ferric Chloride

Ferric Nitrate

Ferric Oxide (black)

Ferric Oxide (Red)

Potassium Dichromate

Silver Nitrate

Sodium Chloride

Sodium Thiosulfate

Stannic Oxide

Sulfurated Potash (Potassium sulfide)

Titanium Oxide (dioxide)

Vinegar (4% to 8% acetic acid)

Water (distilled)

Zinc Nitrate

Footnotes

#1 Steve Van Beck "The Arts of Thailand", (Hong Kong: Travel Publishing Asia Ltd., 1985), page 48.

#2 Richard Hughs and Michael Rowe, "The Colouring, Bronzing and Patination of Metals", (London: The Crafts Council, 1982), page 11.

#3 Mike Excell, Columbia Metals Ltd. "Metallurgia", Volume 39, November 1992), page 407.

#4 R.A. Wilkins and E.S. Bunn, "Copper and Copper Base Alloys", (New York and London: McGraw Hill Book Co., 1943), page 239.

#5 Anaconda American Brass Company, "Copper Metals Data Sheet", Conneticut Sales Promotion Department, Anaconda American Brass Company, Everdur.

#6 Richard Hughs and Michael Rowe, "The Colouring, Bronzing and Patination of Metals", (London: The Crafts Council, 1982), page 24.

#7 Ralph Mayer, "The Artist's Handbook of Materials and Techniques", (New York: Viking Press, ninth printing, 1977), page 618.

#8 Andrew Lins, Article—Outdoor Bronzes: Some Basic Considerations, "Sculptural Monuments In An Outdoor Environment", (Philadelphia: Pennsylvania Academy of The Fine Arts, 1985), page 17.

Bibliography

#1 American Society For Metals, "Metals Handbook", Ninth Edition, Volume 2, American Society For Metals, Metals Park, Ohio, 1979.

#2 Anaconda, "Copper Metals Data Sheet," Anaconda American Brass Company, Waterbury, CT, Everdur.

#3 Copper Development Association, "Application Data Sheet", Copper Development Association, Inc., New York.

#4 d'Argence, Rene-Yvon Lefebvre, "Bronze Vessels of Ancient China", Asian Art Museum of San Francisco, Supported by a grant from the national Endowment for the Arts in Washington, D.C. and the Museum Society, San Francisco,1977.

#5 Edge, Michael "The Art Of Patinas", Artesia Press, Oregon, 1990.

#6 Excell, Mike Columbia Metals Ltd., Silicon Bronze — Versatile, Durable and Easy to Form, "Metallurgia", Vol. 39, No. 11, Nov. 1992.

#7 Fagan, Brian "New Treasures of The Past", Grange Books, London, 1987.

#8 Fishlock, David "Metal Coloring", Robert Draper Ltd., 1970.

#9 Hughs, Richard and Rowe, Michael, "The Colouring, Bronzing And Patination Of Metals", Craft Council, London, 1982.

#10 Juliano, Annette L., "Bronze, Clay and Stone", Hsi An T'ang, University Of Washington Press, Seattle, 1988.

#11 Lewis, Richard J. Sr, "Hawley's Condensed Chemical Dictionary", Van Nostrand Reinhold Co., New York, 1993.

#12 Lins, Andrew Outdoor Bronzes, "Sculptural Monuments In An Outdoor Environment", Pennsylvania Academy Of The Fine Arts, Philadelphia, 1985.

#13 Mayer, Ralph "The Artist's Handbook of Materials and Techniques", The Viking Press, New York, 1977.

#14 Shearman, William, "Metal Alloys and Patinas For Castings", Kent State University Press, Ohio, 1976.

#15 Smith, William F., "Structures and Properties of Engineering Alloys", McGraw-Hill Inc., New York.

#16 Van Beck, Steve, "The Arts of Thailand", Travel Publishing Asia Limited, Hong Kong, 1985.

#17 West, E.G. "Copper And Its Alloys", Ellis Horwood Limited, Chichester, England, 1982.

#18 Wilkins, R.A. & Bunn, E.S., "Copper and Copper Base Alloys", McGraw-Hill Book Co. Inc., New York and London, 1943.

#19 Young, Ronald D., "Contemporary Patination", Sculpt - Nouveau, San Rafael, CA, 1988.